CONTENTS
目录

CENTRAL
中区

SOUTH WEST
西南

SOUTH EAST
东南

NORTH EAST
& NORTH WEST
东北及西北

ONCE UPON A TIME, IN THE HEART OF FRANCE...

It all started way back in 1889, in Clermont-Ferrand, when the Michelin brothers founded the Manufacture Française des Pneumatiques Michelin tyre company – this was at a time when driving was considered quite an adventure!

In 1900, fewer than 3,000 cars existed in France. The Michelin brothers hit upon the idea of creating a small guide packed with useful information for the new pioneers of the road, such as where to fill up with petrol or change a tyre, as well as where to eat and sleep. The MICHELIN Guide was born!

The purpose of the guide was obvious: to track down the best hotels and restaurants across the country. To do this, Michelin employed a veritable armada of anonymous professional inspectors to scour every region – something that had never before been attempted!

Over the years, bumpy roads were replaced by smoother highways and the company continued to develop, as indeed did the country's cuisine: cooks became chefs, artisans developed into artists, and traditional dishes were transformed into works of art. All the while, the MICHELIN Guide, by now a faithful travel companion, kept pace with – and encouraged – these changes. The most famous distinction awarded by the guide was created in 1926: the "étoile de bonne table" – the famous star which quickly established itself as the reference in the world of gastronomy!

Bibendum – the famous tyre-clad Michelin man – continued to widen his reach and by 1911, the guide covered the whole of Europe.

In 2006, the collection crossed the Atlantic, awarding stars to 39 restaurants in New York. In 2007 and 2008, the guide moved on to San Francisco, Los Angeles and Las Vegas, and in 2011 it was the turn of Chicago to have its own Michelin guide – The Michelin Man had become truly American!

In November 2007, The Michelin Man took his first steps in Asia: in recognition of the excellence of Japanese cuisine, stars rained down on Tokyo, which was gripped by culinary fever! A guide to Kyoto, Kobe, Osaka and Nara followed, with Yokohama and Shonan then joining Tokyo. Thereafter the Michelin Man set his feet down in Southern China, with the publication in 2009 of a guide to Hong Kong and Macau.

The Red Guide was now firmly on the map in the Far East. The Michelin Man then explored Southeast Asia and China. In 2016 the first editions of MICHELIN Guide Singapore, MICHELIN Guide Shanghai and MICHELIN Guide Seoul were published. The MICHELIN guides collection now covers 29 titles in 28 countries, with over 30 million copies sold in a century. Quite a record!

Meanwhile, the search continues... Looking for a delicious cassoulet or pot-au-feu in a typical Parisian bistro, or some mouth-watering Singapore street food? The Michelin Man continues to span the globe making new discoveries and selecting the very best the culinary world has to offer!

从前，在法国中部

这一切始于1889年，米其林兄弟在法国克莱蒙费朗（Clermont-Ferrand）创办Manufacture Française des Pneumatiques Michelin 轮胎公司——当年驾驶汽车仍被视为一大冒险。

在1900年，法国的汽车总数量少于3,000辆。米其林兄弟灵机一触，想到为道路驾驶的先驱提供含实用资讯的小指南，如补充汽油或更换轮胎，以至用餐和睡觉的好去处。米其林指南就这样诞生了！

指南的宗旨非常清晰：搜罗全国各地最好的酒店和餐厅。为达目的，米其林招揽了一整队神秘专业评审员，走遍全国每一个角落寻找值得推介的酒店和餐厅，这在当时是前所未有的创举。

多年来，崎岖不平的道路早已被平顺的高速公路取代，米其林公司持续茁壮成长。同时间，全国各地餐饮业的发展亦一日千里：厨子成为大厨、传统手艺成为艺术，传统菜肴亦转化成为艺术杰作。现今米其林指南已成为广受信赖的旅游伙伴，不仅与时并进，更致力推动这些转变。指南中最著名的是早在1926年面世，并迅即成为美食界权威指标的「星级推介」。

由米其林轮胎人必比登为代言人的米其林指南，不断拓展其版图，到1911年已覆盖全欧洲。

2006年，米其林指南系列成功跨越大西洋，授予纽约39家餐厅星级推介。在2007及2008年，米其林指南在三藩市、洛杉矶和拉斯维加斯出版，2011年已拓展至芝加哥，米其林必比登也正式落户美国。

2007年11月，米其林轮胎人首次踏足亚洲，在东京广发星级推介，以表扬日本料理的卓越成就，同时亦掀起美食热潮。其后，旋即推出京都、神户、大阪及奈良指南，并继东京之后推出横滨和湘南指南。香港和澳门指南亦于2009年推出。

2016年，必比登更涉足新加坡、中国和韩国，推出首本米其林新加坡指南、米其林上海指南和首尔指南，令这本以红色为标志的指南，在远东地区的覆盖范围更见广泛。

时至今日，米其林指南系列共计29本，涵盖28个国家，一个世纪以来，总销量超过三千万册。这是个令人鼓舞的纪录！

此时此刻，我们仍然继续对美食的追寻……是巴黎餐厅的美味杂菜锅，还是令人回味无穷的新加坡街头小吃？必比登将会努力不懈，发掘全球美食，为你们挑选最出色的佳肴美馔！

THE MICHELIN GUIDE'S COMMITMENTS

Whether they are in Japan, the USA, China or Europe, our inspectors apply the same criteria to judge the quality of each and every restaurant and hotel that they visit. The MICHELIN guide commands a **worldwide reputation** thanks to the commitments we make to our readers – and we reiterate these below:

Our inspectors make regular and **anonymous visits** to restaurants and hotels to gauge the quality of products and services offered to an ordinary customer. They settle their own bill and may then introduce themselves and ask for more information about the establishment.

To remain totally objective for our readers, the selection is made with complete **independence**. Entry into the guide is free. All decisions are discussed with the Editor and our highest awards are considered at an international level.

The guide offers a **selection** of the best restaurants and hotels in every category of comfort and price. This is only possible because all the inspectors rigorously apply the same methods.

All the practical information, classifications and awards are revised and updated every year to give the most **reliable information** possible.

In order to guarantee the **consistency** of our selection, our classification criteria are the same in every country covered by the MICHELIN guide. Each culture may have its own unique cuisine but **quality** remains the **universal principle** behind our selection.

Michelin's mission is to **aid your mobility**. Our sole aim is to make your journeys safe and pleasurable.

承诺

不论身处日本、美国、中国或欧洲，我们的独立评审员均使用一致的评选方法对餐厅和酒店作出评估。米其林指南在世界各地均享负盛名，关键在其秉承一贯宗旨，履行对读者的承诺：

评审员以匿名方式定期到访餐厅和酒店，以一般顾客的身份对餐厅和酒店的食品和服务素质作出评估。评审员自行结账后，在需要时会介绍自己，并会详细询问有关餐厅或酒店的资料。

为保证本指南以读者利益为依归，餐厅的评选完全是我们独立的决定。我们不会向收录在指南内的餐厅收取任何费用，所有评选经编辑和评审员一同讨论才作出决定，最高级别的评级以国际水平为标准。

本指南推介一系列优质餐厅和酒店，当中含括不同的舒适程度和价格，这全赖一众评审员使用一致且严谨的评选方法。

所有实用资讯、分类及评级都会每年修订和更新，务求为读者提供最可靠的资料。

为确保指南的一致性，每个国家地区均采用相同的评审和分类准则，纵然各地的饮食文化不同，我们评选时的准则完全取决于食物素质和厨师的厨艺。

米其林的目标多年来贯彻始终——致力令旅程尽善尽美，让您在旅游和外出用膳时不但安全，且充满乐趣。

STARS

Our famous One ❀, Two ❀❀ and Three ❀❀❀ Stars
identify establishments serving the highest quality
cuisine – taking into account the quality of ingredients,
the mastery of techniques and flavours, the levels of
creativity and, of course, consistency.

❀❀❀   Exceptional cuisine, worth a special journey!

❀❀   Excellent cuisine, worth a detour!

❀   High quality cooking, worth a stop!

BIB GOURMAND

This symbol indicates our inspectors'
favourites for good value. These restaurants
offer quality cooking for SG$45 or less
(price of a 3 course meal excluding drinks).

PLATE

Good cooking.
Fresh ingredients, capably prepared:
simply a good meal.

THE MICHELIN GUIDE'S SYMBOLS

Michelin are experts at finding the best restaurants and invite you to explore the diversity of the gastronomic universe. As well as evaluating a restaurant's cooking, we also consider its décor, the service and the ambience – in other words, the all-round culinary experience.

Two keywords help you make your choice more quickly: red for the type of cuisine, gold for the atmosphere:

Singaporean • Elegant

FACILITIES & SERVICES

$	Cash only
♿	Wheelchair access
☂	Terrace dining
≼	Interesting view
🅿	Valet parking
P	Car park
🚗	Garage
⊕12	Private room with maximum capacity
⊟	Counter
◐	Reservations required
⊘	Reservations not accepted
≠	Non smoking rooms
♟	Conference rooms
⊠ ⊼	Indoor / Outdoor swimming pool
Spa	Spa
↳	Exercise room
⊙	Casino
⊗	Interesting wine list

米其林图标 ———————

米其林是追寻最佳餐厅的专家,邀请您共同发掘丰富多元的餐饮世界。在品评餐厅烹调素质同时,我们亦将其装潢、服务和整体氛围加入考虑,换言之,是包含味觉、感官和整体用餐经验的全方位评估。

两组关键词助你挑选合适的餐厅,红色为菜式种类;金色是环境氛围:

新加坡菜 · 典雅

设施及服务

🏧	只接受现金
♿	轮椅通道
⛱	阳台用餐
≼	上佳景观
🅿	代客泊车
P	停车场
🚗	室内停车场
⬡12	私人厢房及座位数目
⊟	柜台式
🍴	需订座
🍴	不设订座
⇎	非吸烟房
🧑	会议室
⊠ 🐬	室内 / 室外游泳池
Spa	水疗服务
🏋	健身室
⑤	娱乐场所
🍷	供应优质餐酒

米其林美食评级分类

星级美食

闻名遐迩的米其林一星✽、二星✽✽和三星✽✽✽推介,推荐的是
食物素质特别出色的餐厅。我们的评级考虑到以下因素:材料的
素质和搭配、烹调技巧和味道层次、菜肴所展示的创意,少不了
的是食物水平的一致性。

✽✽✽	卓越的烹调,值得专程造访!
✽✽	烹调出色,不容错过!
✽	优质烹调,不妨一试!

必比登美食推介餐厅

必比登标志表示该餐厅提供具素质且经济
实惠的美食:费用在45元或以下
(三道菜式但不包括饮料)。

米其林餐盘

评审员万里挑一的餐厅,
食材新鲜、烹调用心,菜肴美味。

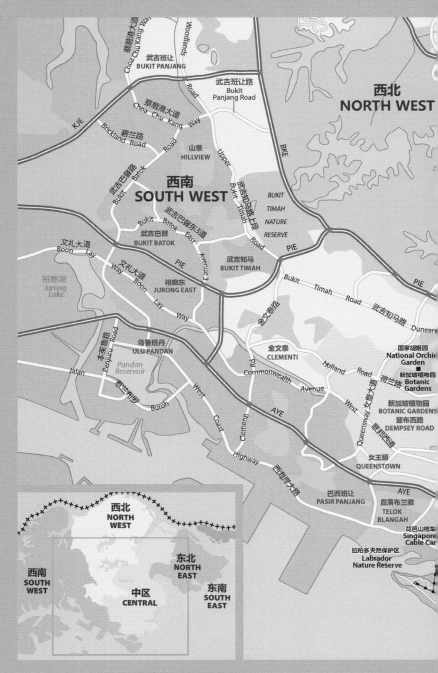

武吉班让
BUKIT PANJANG

蔡厝港六道
Choa Chu Kang Way

Woodlands

武吉班让路
Bukit
Panjang Road

蔡厝港大道
Choa Chu Kang Way

碧兰路
Brickland
Road

KJE

BKE

山景
HILLVIEW

Upper Bukit Timah Road

武吉巴督路
Bukit Batok Road

西北
NORTH WEST

西南
SOUTH WEST

武吉知马上段
Upper Bukit Timah

BUKIT TIMAH NATURE RESERVE

武吉巴督东3道
Bukit Batok East Avenue 3

武吉巴督
BUKIT BATOK

PIE

武吉知马
BUKIT TIMAH

PIE

文礼大道
Boon Lay Way

裕廊湖
Jurong Lake

文礼大道
Boon Lay Way

裕廊东
JURONG EAST

Bukit Timah Road 武吉知马路

Dunear

PIE

武吉巴督东3道

本茱鲁路
Penjuru Road

乌鲁班丹
ULU PANDAN

金文泰路
金文泰
CLEMENTI

国家胡姬园
National Orchid Garden

新加坡植物园
Botanic Gardens

Pandan Reservoir

青兰市路

Jalan Buroh

West Coast Highway

Commonwealth Avenue

Clementi Road

AYE

Holland Road 荷兰路

West Coast Road 女皇大道

新加坡植物园
BOTANIC GARDENS
登布西路
DEMPSEY ROAD

Queensway 女皇大道

联邦西路

女王镇
QUEENSTOWN

AYE

巴西班让
PASIR PANJANG

AYE

直落布兰雅
TELOK BLANGAH

花芭山缆车
Singapore Cable Car

拉柏多天然保护区
Labrador Nature Reserve

西北
NORTH WEST

西南
SOUTH WEST

中区
CENTRAL

东北
NORTH EAST

东南
SOUTH EAST

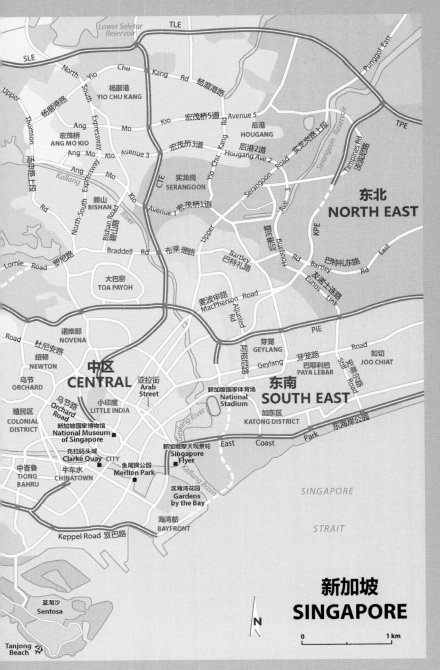

Lower Seletar Reservoir

TLE

SLE

North - Yio Chu Kang Rd 杨厝港路

杨厝港 YIO CHU KANG

Upper Thomson 汤申路上段

杨厝港路 North - South Expressway

Ang Mo Kio Avenue 5 宏茂桥5道

Avenue 5

后港 HOUGANG

宏茂桥 ANG MO KIO

Mo Kio

宏茂桥3道

后港2道

Punggol East

TPE

Ang Mo Kio Avenue 3

宏茂桥3道 Yio Chu Kang

Hougang Ave 2 后港2道

Serangoon Reservoir

Tampines Rd 淡滨尼路

淡滨尼路

Kallang River

Ang Mo Kio

CTE

实龙岗 SERANGOON

实龙岗路 Serangoon Road

实龙岗

东北 NORTH EAST

碧山 BISHAN

North - South Expressway

Bishan Road 碧山路

Avenue 1 宏茂桥1道

Upper

Serangoon Rd

Ave 3

巴特礼东路

KPE

Tampines East

Lornie Road 罗尼路

Braddell Rd 布莱 德路

大巴窑 TOA PAYOH

Bartley 巴特礼路

后港3道 Buangkok Rd

Bartley Rd 友港土连路

Eunos Link

巴特礼东路

麦波申路 MacPherson Road

Aljunied Rd 阿裕尼路

PIE

Road 诺维那 NOVENA

杜尼安路

纽顿 NEWTON

中区 CENTRAL

亚拉街 Arab Street

芽笼 GEYLANG

芽笼路 Geylang

芽笼路

巴耶利巴 PAYA LEBAR

Road

如切 JOO CHIAT

中峇鲁路

乌节 ORCHARD

乌节路 Orchard Road

小印度 LITTLE INDIA

新加坡国家体育场 National Stadium

东南 SOUTH EAST

殖民区 COLONIAL DISTRICT

新加坡国家博物馆 National Museum of Singapore

克拉码头城 Clarke Quay

CITY

牛车水 CHINATOWN

鱼尾狮公园 Merlion Park

加东区 KATONG DISTRICT

Geylang River

East Coast Park 东海岸公园

中峇鲁 TIONG BAHRU

新加坡摩天观景轮 Singapore Flyer

滨海湾花园 Gardens by the Bay

East Coast Park

Kallang Basin

SINGAPORE

STRAIT

海湾舫 BAYFRONT

Keppel Road 岌巴路

圣淘沙 Sentosa

N

新加坡 SINGAPORE

0   1 km

Tanjong Beach

RESTAURANTS, HAWKER CENTRES, STREET FOOD & HOTELS... OUR SELECTION BY DISTRICT

餐厅、熟食小贩中心、街头小吃及酒店……以地区分类

Rainer Kiedrowski/Bildarchiv Monheim / age fotostock

CENTRAL
中区

RESTAURANTS
餐厅

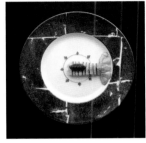

❀ ❀

LES AMIS
French • Elegant
法国菜 • 典雅

Les Amis is as good-looking today as it was when it opened in 1994. This singularly sophisticated and world renowned restaurant is spread over two floors and is run with impeccable attention to detail. The set menus offer classical French cuisine with the occasional Asian influence; signature dishes include caviar on angel hair pasta and pâté en croûte. The stunning wine list is one of the best in Asia.

满目的艺术品和画作、华丽的天鹅绒墙壁、天花上的水晶吊灯和专业优雅的服务，营造了惬意浪漫的环境。法籍主厨擅于展示时令食材的天然风味，巧妙地将法国传统和日式风格融合于菜式上，招牌菜有鱼子酱天使面及鸭肝酱批。餐酒选择之多使人心猿意马。

⇔35 ◐Ⅱ ❀
TEL. 6733 2225
Shaw Centre, #01-16, 1 Scotts Road
史各士路1号邵氏中心 #01-16
www.lesamis.com.sg

CENTRAL 中区

■ **PRICE** 价钱
Lunch 午膳
set 套餐 $ 85-205
Dinner 晚膳
set 套餐 $ 185-340
à la carte 点菜 $ 245-365

■ **OPENING HOURS** 营业时间
Lunch 午膳 12:00-13:45 (L.O.)
Dinner 晚膳 19:00-20:45 (L.O.)

FoodCollection / Photononstop

TEL. 6385 0498

National Gallery Singapore, #01-04, 1 St. Andrew's Road (entrance via Supreme Court wing's foyer)
圣安德烈路1号国家美术馆#01-04 (Supreme Court wing's foyer入口)
www.odetterestaurant.com

■ **PRICE 价钱**
Lunch 午膳
set 套餐 $ 128-188
Dinner 晚膳
set 套餐 $ 268-328

■ **OPENING HOURS 营业时间**
Lunch 午膳 12:00-13:15 (L.O.)
Dinner 晚膳 19:00-20:30 (L.O.)

■ **ANNUAL AND WEEKLY CLOSING**
休息日期
Closed Monday lunch; Sunday and Public Holidays
周一午膳;周日及公众假期休息

✿ ✿

ODETTE

French contemporary • Elegant
时尚法国菜•典雅

What was once the registration room of the Supreme Court is now the most discreet and intimate of restaurants – named by Chef Julien Royer after his grandmother. His artfully presented modern cuisine shows plenty of finesse and uses subtle Japanese influences. Fish is from Japan and New Zealand and only the best organic produce from local farms makes it to the table. Try his signature pigeon dishes, available year round with seasonal garnishes.

曾是高等法院的登记处,如今是这家高雅餐厅的所在。透过玻璃门,食客可观摩厨师们在厨房奋力工作的情景。厨师Julien Royer的菜式有着精雕细琢的摆盘设计,且糅合了日本元素。只有上乘的食材才会被选用,包括来自有机农场的产物,或进口自日本、新西兰的鱼获。不妨点选四季皆供应、并随季节转换搭配的乳鸽菜式。

SHISEN HANTEN
四川飯店

Chinese · Contemporary

中国菜 · 时尚

TEL. 6831 6262

**Mandarin Orchard Hotel,
Orchard Wing, Level 35,
333 Orchard Road**
乌节路333号文华大酒店35层
www.shisenhanten.com.sg

The Mandarin Orchard hotel plays host to the first overseas branch of this Sichuan restaurant group from Japan. Crystal chandeliers and high ceilings add a certain grandeur to a room which is perched on the 35th floor – ask for a window table for the city views. The Sichuan specialities include steamed fish with diced hot red peppers and stewed beef in hot pepper sauce – but it is 'Chen's Mapo Doufu' which is not to be missed.

为日本四川饭店在国外首间分店。餐厅位于酒店较高楼层，主餐室高耸的天花和水晶吊灯别具气派，两边窗户可饱览城市景色。菜式以川菜为主，如水煮菜式和剁椒蒸鲈鱼等，招牌菜陈麻婆豆腐绝不能错过，此外也提供受欢迎的中国菜如北京烤鸭和广式烧味。设四间私人厢房，建议预订主餐室两边靠窗位置。

■ **PRICE** 价钱
Lunch 午膳
set 套餐 $ 45-60
à la carte 点菜 $ 60-110
Dinner 晚膳
à la carte 点菜 $ 60-110

■ **OPENING HOURS** 营业时间
Lunch 午膳 12:00-14:30 (L.O.)
Weekend & Public Holidays lunch
周末及公众假期午膳
11:00-14:30 (L.O.)
Dinner 晚膳 18:00-21:45 (L.O.)

CENTRAL 中区

CENTRAL 中区

P ⇌6 ⇌ ☺↑↑
TEL. 6423 9939

One Fullerton, #02-02A,
1 Fullerton Road
浮尔顿路1号浮尔顿一号#02-02A
www.shoukouwa.com.sg

■ **PRICE 价钱**
Lunch 午膳
set 套餐 $ 180
Dinner 晚膳
set 套餐 $ 320-480

■ **OPENING HOURS 营业时间**
Lunch 午膳 12:00-13:30 (L.O.)
Dinner 晚膳 18:00-20:00 (L.O.)

■ **ANNUAL AND WEEKLY CLOSING**
休息日期
Closed Sunday lunch and Monday
周日午膳及周一休息

SHOUKOUWA
小康和

Sushi • Minimalist
寿司 • 简约

Not only will you leave feeling wholly satisfied and fulfilled after eating at this Japanese restaurant, but you'll also be fully aware that the ingredients you've just enjoyed were of the highest quality possible. The counter seats just 8 people and you're treated to an expertly balanced seasonal omakase, with fish flown in from Tokyo's Tsukiji market on a daily basis. It's located next to the iconic Merlion.

精巧细小的店子，设计简约，只有一张寿司柜台。台前设有八个座位，台后是厨师大展身手的舞台。店内使用的食材全是每天从日本筑地鱼市场空运而来，素质高兼非常新鲜。造诣精湛的厨师专注而细心地处理食材，为食客奉上质优味美且最时令的厨师发办套餐，高素质的烹调和食材，实在物有所值。

WAKU GHIN

Japanese contemporary • Elegant

时尚日本菜•典雅

Gather up all your winnings at the casino – for you will need them – and head to this sophisticated Japanese restaurant from Tetsuya Wakuda, known for his eponymous place in Sydney. The restaurant comprises four rooms and a tasting menu is offered. There is no doubting the exceptional quality of ingredients, in dishes like Botan shrimps with sea urchin and Oscietra caviar, and Japanese Ohmi Wagyu beef with wasabi and citrus soy.

这家由祖籍日本的澳洲厨师久田哲也继悉尼原店后开设的餐厅，品尝菜单以时令食材制作，材料分别来自日本、澳洲、加拿大和法国。招牌菜有oscietra鱼子酱海胆牡丹虾及芥末近江和牛。无微不至的服务、美味得超乎想像的味道和极致高级的食材，加起来令在此的用餐经验无可比拟。

  ♿ 🅿 ♻12 🍴 🕐❙ 🍸

TEL. 6688 8507

The Shoppes at Marina Bay Sands,
Level 2 Dining, L2-01,
10 Bayfront Avenue

贝弗兰道10号金沙酒店
金沙购物商城中庭楼层2 L2-01

www.marinabaysands.com

■ **PRICE** 价钱
Dinner 晚膳
set 套餐 $ 450

■ **OPENING HOURS** 营业时间
Dinner 晚膳 17:30-19:30;
20:00-22:00

CENTRAL 中区

CENTRAL 中区

🏠 🅿 ⟷14 ◐🍴 ⋙

TEL. 6735 9937

**Goodwood Park Hotel,
22 Scotts Road**
史各士路22号良木园酒店
www.alma.sg

■ **PRICE 价钱**
Lunch 午膳
set 套餐 $ 39-50
Dinner 晚膳
set 套餐 $ 138-178

■ **OPENING HOURS 营业时间**
Lunch 午膳 12:00-14:30 (L.O.)
Dinner 晚膳 18:00-21:30 (L.O.)

■ **ANNUAL AND WEEKLY CLOSING**
休息日期
Closed Saturday lunch and Sunday
周六午膳及周日休息

ALMA

European contemporary • Fashionable
时尚欧陆菜 • 时髦

A new team took over this space at the Goodwood Park hotel in 2016 and with it came new-look menus offering 6 or 8 courses at dinner, and a limited choice at lunch. The influences on the cuisine are largely European and contemporary and the ingredients are well chosen. The signature dishes include cold angel hair pasta with seaweed and lobster; lamb tartare with goat's cheese and tomato chutney; and crispy tofu with wild mushroom, black garlic and foie gras.

餐厅划分为数个部分：主要用餐区以深色木家具配以橙黑色餐椅，柔和舒适；酒窖后为私人厢房；另设户外用餐区，可以边喝酒边享用Tapas。午餐供应三道菜的套餐，晚餐则可选六或八道菜的套餐。招牌菜包括波士顿龙虾海带冻天使面、羊肉他他配山羊奶酪酸辣酱及野菌鹅肝脆豆腐。

BÉNI
French contemporary • Minimalist
时尚法国菜·简约

In the Mandarin Gallery, this small, elegant restaurant offers contemporary French cuisine. The minimalist décor is designed so as not to detract from the food and the counter allows guests to watch the chefs go about their work. The top quality seasonal ingredients come largely from France and Japan and the two set menus change on a weekly basis.

长方形木制桌子，带有浓浓的日本风格。这儿不设点菜，只提供两款餐牌。主厨对食材有一份执着，采用的全是高素质的时令食材，大部分材料来自法国及日本。酒单丰富多样，更提供Royal Blue Tea。店内有两间私人厢房。

P ⟷10 🚗 ◐🏠
TEL. 9159 3177

**Mandarin Gallery, #02-37,
333A Orchard Road**
乌节路333A号文华购物廊#02-37
www.beni-sg.com

■ **PRICE** 价钱
Lunch 午膳
set 套餐 $ 68-228
Dinner 晚膳
set 套餐 $ 178-258

■ **OPENING HOURS** 营业时间
Lunch 午膳 12:00-13:30 (L.O.)
Dinner 晚膳 19:00-20:30 (L.O.)

■ **ANNUAL AND WEEKLY CLOSING**
休息日期
Closed Sunday 周日休息

CENTRAL 中区

CENTRAL 中区

⟨⟨ ⟨Ⓞ⟩⏌

TEL. 6866 1933

Level 5, 52 Boat Quay

驳船码头52号5层

www.braci.sg

■ **PRICE 价钱**
Lunch 午膳
set 套餐 $ 55-200
à la carte 点菜 $ 90-160
Dinner 晚膳
set 套餐 $ 100-200
à la carte 点菜 $ 90-160

■ **OPENING HOURS 营业时间**
Lunch 午膳 12:00-14:00 (L.O.)
Dinner 晚膳 18:00-21:30 (L.O.)

■ **ANNUAL AND WEEKLY CLOSING**
休息日期
Closed Monday & Saturday lunch;
Sunday and Public Holidays
周一及周六午膳、周日及公众假期休
息

BRACI

Italian contemporary · Design
时尚意大利菜·型格

Beppe De Vito considers his cuisine a 'culinary journey', taking customers in his tiny dining room from the South of Italy to Asia via some interesting detours. Choose one of the set menus and let the kitchen decide; it could include tuna millefeuille with truffles, foie gras semi-freddo or sea bass with eggplant parmigiana. A pre-dinner drink on the rooftop terrace of this charming shophouse, to take in the terrific river views, is a must.

店内只有十六个座位，开放式厨房占用了1/3的空间。咖啡色木墙、面向河景的大窗和简单的布置，简约时尚。来自普利亚的厨师受到家里的熏陶，烹调风格充满意国南部色彩，却又带点亚洲风情。帕尔马干酪茄子鲈鱼番红花汁及无花果金橘冻鹅肝是招牌菜。进餐前必定要到天台户外座位喝一杯兼欣赏迷人的河景。

BURNT ENDS

Barbecue • Trendy

烧烤 • 前卫

Meat is what they do best at this Australian-styled BBQ restaurant, thanks to its array of heavy-duty wood-fired ovens and grills - counter seating opposite the kitchen lets you take in the aroma and feel the heat. Don't miss the beef, marmalade and pickles; the flank with burnt onion; the suckling pig; and the bone marrow bun. The funky soundtrack is suitably hip and the all-Aussie wine list offers a concise and esoteric choice.

以600度高温的碳炉及木碳烧烤食物是这儿的特点。看似简单的菜式，透过食材的选配和一丝不苟的烹调显出心思与技巧。橘子酱烟熏甜牛肉令你没齿难忘，焦糖洋葱牛腩牛骨髓口感嫩滑、入口即化，烤乳猪和牛骨髓包亦不能错过。狭长的餐室只以木餐柜台将客人和厨师分隔，食客能边享用美食边观赏厨师烹调时的风采。

TEL. 6224 3933

20 Teck Lim Road

德霖路20号

www.burntends.com.sg

■ **PRICE** 价钱

Lunch 午膳
set 套餐 $ 150-250
à la carte 点菜 $ 50-100
Dinner 晚膳
set 套餐 $ 150-250
à la carte 点菜 $ 70-190

■ **OPENING HOURS** 营业时间

Lunch 午膳 11:45-14:00 (L.O.)
Dinner 晚膳 18:00-00:00 (L.O.)

■ **ANNUAL AND WEEKLY CLOSING** 休息日期

Closed Tuesday to Thursday lunch; Sunday and Monday
周二至周四午膳、周日及周一休息

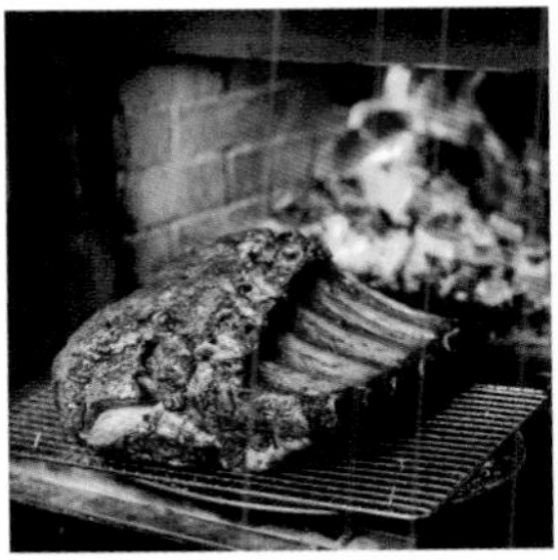

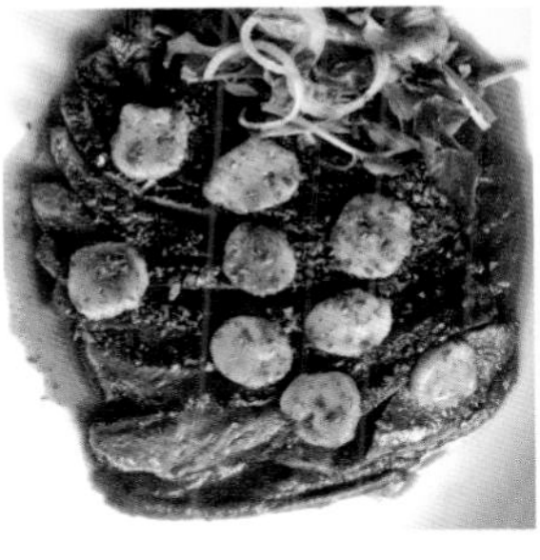

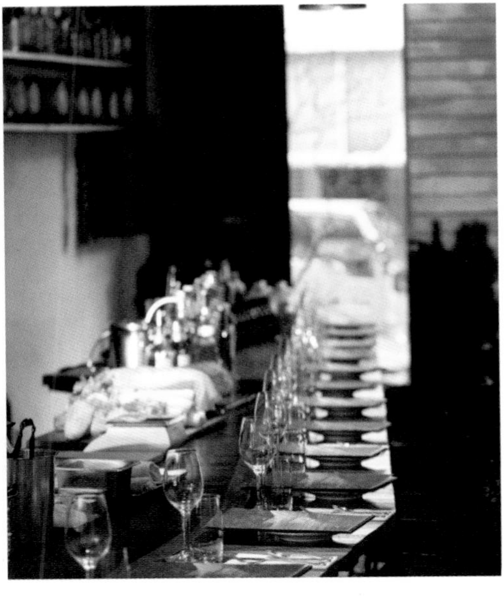

CENTRAL 中区

P ⇦8 ◎⸸

TEL. 1800 304 2288

Block 17A, Dempsey Road
登布西路17号A

■ **PRICE** 价钱
Lunch 午膳
à la carte 点菜 $ 20-60
Dinner 晚膳
set 套餐 $ 118

■ **OPENING HOURS** 营业时间
Lunch 午膳 12:00-14:30 (L.O.)
Dinner 晚膳 18:00-21:30 (L.O.)
Friday & Saturday dinner
周五及周六晚膳 18:00-22:30 (L.O.)

CANDLENUT

Peranakan • Classic
娘惹菜 • 经典

The high ceiling makes the dining room feel open and spacious, while bamboo lampshades and wooden tables add a sense of serenity. Influenced by his mother and grandma, the young chef cooks traditional Peranakan fare with a creative twist and an Indonesian touch. The menu features many one-bite dishes, with up to 100 combinations. Those having difficulty making a choice can opt for the 20-course tasting menu. Service is warm and friendly.

高耸的楼底让餐厅空间显得份外宽敞，竹吊灯搭木桌的布置，感觉轻松。年轻的新加坡籍主厨自小受母亲和祖母熏陶，烹调风格带印尼特色，其娘惹菜既有新意亦不失传统风味。新推出的菜单有不少一口菜式，分量少但配搭多至百种，让客人能尝试不同味道和质感的佳肴。点选品尝菜单(tasting menu)便能尝到二十款菜式。服务团队待客的热诚更令你倍增好感。

CHEEK BY JOWL

Australian contemporary · Friendly

时尚澳洲菜·友善

The husband and wife team chose the name to reflect how closely they work together. Rishi is originally from Sri Lanka but spent his working life in Australia; his 'modern Australian' cuisine is far more complex than it at first seems and his confidence in the ingredients pays dividends in fresh tasting dishes that display a number of influences. Lunch is quite a corporate affair so come for dinner to best experience the kitchen's ability.

凭着一切从简的信念,主厨兼店东Rishi纯以巧妙的厨艺制作出香气四溢且感觉清新的食物。地点靠近商业区,午市时是上班族的据点,喜欢在较安静的环境用餐,请考虑晚市时段到访。午市的二、三及五道菜套餐物有所值。精选酒单罗列的是以风格排序的新世界葡萄酒。负责接待的店东妻子待客随和友善。

TEL. 6221 1911
21 Boon Tat Street
文达街21号
www.cheekbyjowl.com.sg

■ **PRICE** 价钱
Lunch 午膳
set 套餐 $ 38-58
Dinner 晚膳
set 套餐 $ 78-108

■ **OPENING HOURS** 营业时间
Lunch 午膳 11:30-14:30 (L.O.)
Dinner 晚膳 18:00-22:00 (L.O.)

■ **ANNUAL AND WEEKLY CLOSING**
休息日期
Closed Saturday lunch and Sunday
周六午膳及周日休息

CENTRAL 中区

♿12 ◔〒
TEL. 6238 6263
25 Mackenzie Road
麦肯西路25号

■ **PRICE** 价钱
Lunch 午膳
à la carte 点菜 $ 80-100
Dinner 晚膳
à la carte 点菜 $ 100-120

■ **OPENING HOURS** 营业时间
Lunch 午膳 11:30-14:00 (L.O.)
Dinner 晚膳 18:00-22:00 (L.O.)

■ **ANNUAL AND WEEKLY CLOSING**
休息日期
Closed Monday 周一休息

CENTRAL 中区

CHEF KANG'S
江师傅

Cantonese · Simple
粤菜 · 简朴

Chef Kang brings his experience of over 40 years to bear at this simply furnished eatery. The room is more about practicality than luxury – and likewise his cooking largely eschews expensive ingredients to focus instead on creating traditional and satisfying Cantonese dishes. His many loyal customers vouch for his ability – follow their lead and go on a culinary trip by opting for his 'omakase' menu.

毫不沾染世俗尘烟的小店、门牌亦简单地以「江师傅」作招徕。顾名思义,江师傅就是这儿的主厨,他对烹饪有一份坚持,从不假手于人,更会亲自到市场采购食材,甚至不惜功本购入各种野生鱼类,让客人品尝到有素质且味美的菜肴。订座时切记询问哪些时令菜式需要预订,五人或以上建议尝尝厨师发办。

CORNER HOUSE

Innovative · Elegant

创新菜·典雅

When your restaurant occupies a colonial house, dating from 1910, within the Botanic Gardens, it stands to reason the kitchen will have an in-depth understanding of how best to use herbs and plants in the cooking process – indeed, the chef himself describes his contemporary cuisine as 'gastro-botanica'. There's a choice of three rooms: Claret Corner, The Verandah or Whispering Corner which overlooks the patio and is ideal for a romantic dinner.

餐厅位于新加坡植物园、一幢两层高的黑白色殖民地平房内，窗外一片绿油油，餐碟亦仿如一盘盛放的鲜花，因为年轻的主厨喜以香草和食用花卉入馔。不设点菜，套餐均采用来自法国和日本的顶级时令食材，定时更换菜式，例如珍珠洋葱(Oignon doux des Cévennes)会制成烤松露洋葱杯、洋葱茶等。酒单令人目不暇给。

TEL. 6469 1000

Singapore Botanic Gardens (Nassim Gate entrance), 1 Cluny Road

克伦尼路1号新加坡植物园（那森路入口）

www.cornerhouse.com.sg

■ **PRICE** 价钱
Lunch 午膳
set 套餐 $ 62-148
Dinner 晚膳
set 套餐 $ 158-268

■ **OPENING HOURS** 营业时间
Lunch 午膳 12:00-14:00 (L.O.)
Dinner 晚膳 18:30-21:30 (L.O.)

■ **ANNUAL AND WEEKLY CLOSING**
休息日期
Closed 4 days Lunar New Year and Monday 农历新年4天及周一休息

CENTRAL 中区

♿ **P** ↺15 Ⓡ🍴

TEL. 6734 6866

Paragon Shopping Centre, #05-22,
290 Orchard Road
乌节路290号百利宫#05-22

www.crystaljade.com

■ **PRICE** 价钱
Lunch 午膳
set 套餐 $ 48
à la carte 点菜 $ 50-100
Dinner 晚膳
à la carte 点菜 $ 70-150

■ **OPENING HOURS** 营业时间
Lunch 午膳 11:30-14:30 (L.O.)
Dinner 晚膳 18:00-22:00 (L.O.)

■ **ANNUAL AND WEEKLY CLOSING**
休息日期
Closed 1 day Lunar New Year
农历新年休息1天

✿

CRYSTAL JADE GOLDEN PALACE
翡翠金閣

Chinese • Contemporary
中国菜·时尚

Opened in 2002, this is the most comfortable branch of this restaurant group and the only one which specialises in Teochew dishes, like cold crab and sugar-coated yam. Look out too for the Cantonese barbecue meat and assorted seafood dishes; more contemporary offerings include chilled foie gras with sake and roasted suckling pig with black truffle. Their wine cellar includes a good international selection.

集团内唯一一间有潮州菜供应的食府,餐单上大部分均是传统潮州菜如冻蟹、反沙芋等,还有粤式烧味、海鲜菜式和午市的即制点心,此外,还有一些较新派的菜式如清酒鹅肝、黑松露乳猪饭卷等,不妨一试。

CUT

Steakhouse • Fashionable

扒房•时髦

The bone marrow flan with mushroom marmalade at this luxurious steakhouse from Wolfgang Puck may be just as good as the LA original, but you're really here for the eating of beef. Steaks are expertly seasoned and grilled over charcoal before being finished off under a 1200 degree broiler to leave them succulent, tender and juicy. The wine list offers over 650 labels. You can also eat at the counter in the more casual bar.

以1,200度炭火烤炙的牛肉，汁丰肉嫩；恰到好处的调味，进食后齿颊仍留有余香！北海道带子片、杂菌酱牛骨髓、来自神户或本州的A5和牛及纽约西冷是招牌菜。餐酒单供应逾650款佳酿。响亮的音乐让餐室显得热闹，爱静的食客或会感到聒噪。想随意一点，可选择于只有柜台座位的酒吧那边用餐。

♿ 🍽 🅿 ↔40 🚘 🍲 &#x6B

TEL. 6688 8517

The Shoppes at Marina Bay Sands, Galleria Level, B1-71, 2 Bayfront Avenue

贝弗兰道2号滨海湾
金沙购物商城B1-71

www.wolfgangpuck.com/dining/ cut-singapore/

■ **PRICE** 价钱
Dinner 晚膳
à la carte 点菜 $ 98-350

■ **OPENING HOURS** 营业时间
Dinner 晚膳 17:30-22:00 (L.O.)
Friday & Saturday dinner
周五及周六晚膳 17:30-23:00 (L.O.)

CENTRAL 中区

CENTRAL 中区

🍴 ⇔80 🍷 ❦

TEL. 6837 1468

#01-02, 36 Purvis Street
巴米士街36号#01-02

www.garibaldi.com.sg

■ **PRICE 价钱**
Lunch 午膳
set 套餐 $ 39
à la carte 点菜 $ 65-190
Dinner 晚膳
set 套餐 $ 158-218
à la carte 点菜 $ 65-190

■ **OPENING HOURS 营业时间**
Lunch 午膳 12:00-14:30 (L.O.)
Dinner 晚膳 18:30-22:30 (L.O.)

GARIBALDI

Italian • Contemporary
意大利菜 • 时尚

Ossobuco, costoletta alla Milanese and tiramisu are some of the signature dishes here at one of the city's best known Italian restaurants. The affable owner, though, wants everyone to be able to find their favourite dish which is why he offers such a large, all-encompassing menu. The impressive wine list, featuring around 7000 labels, is another feature for which this cosy and contemporary-styled restaurant is celebrated.

店东兼主厨年轻时曾于欧亚多个国家跟随多位意大利名厨工作，造就了此家在本地名闻遐迩的意大利餐馆。选用的食材大部分来自意大利。藏红花牛肘烩饭(Ossobuco)、米兰炸猪排(Costoletta alla Milanese)及提拉米苏是其名菜。任职品酒师的店东妻子帮忙挑选的酒单，涵盖约七千款意大利及法国名酿。

IGGY'S

European contemporary • *Elegant*
时尚欧陆菜 • 典雅

Behind a discreet black door, hidden within the Hilton hotel, is one of Singapore's best known restaurants, which was given a major overhaul in 2016. The contemporary and elegant look includes a large window looking into the kitchen. The cuisine may appear quite simple but there's a lot of technique behind it and the ingredients are top class. Dishes to look out for include 'carabinero rice' and Spanish mackerel with tapioca pearls.

翻新后的餐厅,透着时尚典雅气息。新的团队让食客从服务至食物都有崭新体验。碟上的食物看似简单,却是精湛的厨艺与高素质食材的结合。餐单随季节更换。Iggy's风格小吃、Carabinero意大利饭、马鲛鱼木薯珍珠多蜜酱汁是招牌菜。偌大的玻璃窗让你观看厨房内的景致。

🪑16 ♿ ⊙🍴 🎷

TEL. 6732 2234

Hilton Hotel, Level 3,
581 Orchard Road
乌节路581号希尔顿酒店3层
www.iggys.com.sg

■ **PRICE** 价钱
Lunch 午膳
set 套餐 $ 85-105
Dinner 晚膳
set 套餐 $ 145-238

■ **OPENING HOURS** 营业时间
Lunch 午膳 12:00-13:30 (L.O.)
Dinner 晚膳 19:00-21:30 (L.O.)

■ **ANNUAL AND WEEKLY CLOSING**
休息日期
Closed Monday, Sunday and Public Holidays
周一、周日及公众假期休息

CENTRAL 中区

ᯓ P ⇕14 ◐🍴

TEL. 6736 2118

ION Orchard, #03-05,
2 Orchard Turn

乌节弯路2号乌节Ion大厦#03-05

www.imperialtreasure.com

■ **PRICE** 价钱

Lunch 午膳
à la carte 点菜 $ 30-40
Dinner 晚膳
à la carte 点菜 $ 60-70

■ **OPENING HOURS** 营业时间

Lunch 午膳 11:30-14:45 (L.O.)
Dinner 晚膳 18:00-22:00 (L.O.)

CENTRAL 中区

IMPERIAL TREASURE FINE TEOCHEW CUISINE (ORCHARD)
御寶閣 (乌节)

Teochew • Contemporary
潮州菜 • 时尚

It may have moved to new premises in a large shopping mall at the end of 2016, but this pleasantly dressed Teochew restaurant is bright and relaxing, thanks to its large windows. It offers various traditional Teochew dishes, including some which are not so easy to find these days, like pan-fried taro with prawns or steamed cold mud crabs. With some dishes, you have the option of ordering a smaller portion.

于2016年迁至区内更大型的商场内,室内设计焕然一新,大片玻璃窗引入自然光,气氛轻松。餐厅供应的传统潮州菜选择丰富,个别菜式如惹味香脆的鲜虾芋头焗及每日限量供应的鲜滑冻黄膏蟹,并不常见。此外,大部分菜式都有大、小分量供应,让食客点菜时更有弹性。

JAAN

French contemporary · *Contemporary*
时尚法国菜 · 时尚

Be sure to ask for a window table as this romantic and intimate restaurant is perched on the 70th floor of one of Asia's highest hotels. Its modern menus offer innovative and elaborate dishes and are driven by the ingredients, which are flown in from around the world. There's also a creative vegetarian menu and, if you like surprises, a 'Menu Epicure'. Service is smooth and attentive but refreshingly free from any undue pomp or ceremony.

集时尚、温馨、浪漫于一的设计，晚间情调尤为动人。欲欣赏最佳景致，请提早预订窗边的座位。来自世界各地的高级食材完美地烘托起厨师悉心制作的创新精细菜式。特别创作的素菜餐单、库克香槟配对餐及以惊喜形式呈献的招牌菜美食家餐单 (Epicuremenu)，各有各精彩。服务细心而恰到好处。

← ⌂ 8 ◐⁩ ⅍

TEL. 6837 3322

Swissôtel The Stamford,
Equinox Complex, Level 70,
2 Stamford Road
史丹福路2号史丹福瑞士酒店70层
www.jaan.com.sg

■ PRICE 价钱
Lunch 午膳
set 套餐 $ 88-158
Dinner 晚膳
set 套餐 $ 238-298

■ OPENING HOURS 营业时间
Lunch 午膳 12:00-13:30 (L.O.)
Dinner 晚膳 19:00-21:00 (L.O.)

■ ANNUAL AND WEEKLY CLOSING
休息日期
Closed Sunday and Public Holidays
周日及公众假期休息

CENTRAL 中区

45

♿ 🥢 **P** ⇔22 ◎🍴

TEL. 6831 7250

**Four Seasons Hotel, Level 2,
190 Orchard Boulevard**

乌节林荫道190号四季酒店2层

www.fourseasons.com/singapore

■ **PRICE** 价钱
Lunch 午膳
set 套餐 $ 138-258
à la carte 点菜 $ 80-250
Dinner 晚膳
set 套餐 $ 138-258
à la carte 点菜 $ 80-250

■ **OPENING HOURS** 营业时间
Lunch 午膳 11:30-14:00 (L.O.)
Dinner 晚膳 18:00-22:00 (L.O.)

JIANG-NAN CHUN
江南春

Cantonese · Luxury
粤菜 · 豪华

The exquisite space, reached via a marble staircase, is warm and welcoming and its heavy leather chairs are especially comfortable. In 2017 Chef Lam, with over 20 years' experience in Cantonese cooking, joined the kitchen. Apart from traditional dishes, his signatures like deep-fried chicken with fresh lemon sauce and wok-fried star grouper fillet with superior soy sauce are obvious highlights. Reservations recommended.

从四季酒店第一层的大理石楷梯拾级而上即可到达。餐厅富亚洲风情，装饰雅致温暖，厚厚的皮革座椅予人舒适之感。餐单以粤菜为主，主理广东菜逾二十年的林师傅于2017年加盟后，除了保留传统广东菜外，更加添了其首本名菜，包括鲜柠汁脆皮炸子鸡及头抽干煎东星件。餐厅不论何时皆坐无虚席，建议订座。

CENTRAL 中区

LABYRINTH

Innovative • Modern

创新菜 • 现代

If you want a modern take on Singaporean cuisine, this is your place. Flavours are bold yet authentic and the presentation is highly artistic. The contemporary dining room, with its local artwork, makes you feel as though you're in on something secret, while the small bar is a great spot for a breezy cocktail and a chance to chat to the keen, well-informed staff about what awaits.

创新方式演绎的食物，从外观上看令人疑惑，不知所吃为何物，然而品尝一下，风味却传统可口，让你再三回味。大厨从祖母身上得到启发的创意凤梨炒饭并不是常见的凤梨炒饭：意式蛋黄酱、凤梨雪芭、葡萄干、腰果及米通，味道与分量调配得刚好，颇有特色。

TEL. 6223 4098

Esplanade Mall, #02-23,
Marina Bay Promenade,
8 Raffles Avenue

莱佛士道8号
滨海艺术中心购物坊#02-23

www.labyrinth.com.sg

■ **PRICE** 价钱
Lunch 午膳
set 套餐 $ 58-68
Dinner 晚膳
set 套餐 $ 68-118

■ **OPENING HOURS** 营业时间
Lunch 午膳 12:00-13:30 (L.O.)
Dinner 晚膳 18:30-21:00 (L.O.)

■ **ANNUAL AND WEEKLY CLOSING**
休息日期
Closed 4 days Lunar New Year,
Weekend lunch and Monday
农历新年4天、周末午膳及周一休息

CENTRAL 中区

🍴 ⇦12 ⓄⅡ

TEL. 6339 3822

Chijmes, #01-24, 30 Victoria Street

维多利亚街30号赞美广场#01-24

www.leigarden.com.cn

■ **PRICE** 价钱
Lunch 午膳
à la carte 点菜 $ 30-90
Dinner 晚膳
à la carte 点菜 $ 30-90

■ **OPENING HOURS** 营业时间
Lunch 午膳 11:30-14:30 (L.O.)
Dinner 晚膳 18:00-21:30 (L.O.)

■ **ANNUAL AND WEEKLY CLOSING**
休息日期
Closed 3 days Lunar New Year
农历新年休息3天

LEI GARDEN
利苑
Cantonese • Contemporary
粤菜 • 时尚

Unlike the other restaurants in the group, this one comes with a more European feel to its decoration, in keeping with the colonial style of the building which hosts it. What isn't different from the other branches is the menu content – so expect authentic Cantonese dishes prepared with care and good quality dim sum at lunch. It's certainly worth ordering the roasted meats and the double-boiled soups in advance.

此店的室内设计有别于集团一贯的中国风,为了与所在的殖民地建筑物互相融合,布置装潢均充满欧陆气息。然而,餐单上的菜式却与集团其他分店没什分别,食物的味道是一贯的正宗,建议预订粤式烧味和炖汤。午市点心同样吸引。

ASIA'S ULTIMATE LIFESTYLE DESTINATION

Resorts World Sentosa is where you will find a curation of the finest experiences. Connoisseurs will appreciate meals at celebrity chef and Michelin-starred establishments, where a celebration of international culinary art of the highest order is a daily affair. Once you are energised, enjoy endless excitement at world-class attractions like Universal Studios Singapore, S.E.A. Aquarium, Adventure Cove Waterpark, The Maritime Experiential Museum and Dolphin Island. After all your activity, recharge in luxurious accommodation as you are spoiled by stellar service in great hotels. Rest well, for another beautiful day full of wonders await.

World-class Attractions

Luxurious Accommodation

Michelin-starred Cuisine

www.rwsentosa.com

MA CUISINE

French • Bistro

法国菜 • 法式小餐馆

This white shophouse, with its traditional bistro décor, is heaven for oenophiles – the first thing diners are offered upon being seated is a phonebook-like wine menu. Servers are keen to walk you through every vineyard and vintage and their deep knowledge makes the experience unique. By comparison, the food menu is concise with French classics sitting alongside daily specials and a cocotte of the day, to complement your wine choices.

餐厅位于一幢白色外墙建筑之内，置于四周的酒瓶和酒桶点出了美酒在这里的显著地位，就座后，迎来的是厚甸甸的酒单，各国佳酿琳琅满目，心猿意马的食客大可请知识丰富的服务员助你一把。食物方面，简短而精巧的餐单上是法国经典菜肴，不妨点选每日精选来搭配佳酿。

TEL. 6224 1838

38 Craig Road

克力路38号

macuisinesg.com

■ **PRICE** 价钱
Dinner 晚膳
à la carte 点菜 $ 40-75

■ **OPENING HOURS** 营业时间
Dinner 晚膳 17:30-23:30 (L.O.)

■ **ANNUAL AND WEEKLY CLOSING**
休息日期
Closed Labour Day and Sunday
劳动节及周日休息

CENTRAL 中区

🚍 ☕❚

TEL. 6513 0898

9 Keong Saik Road

恭锡路9号

www.metarestaurant.sg

■ **PRICE 价钱**
Lunch 午膳
set 套餐 $ 52
Dinner 晚膳
set 套餐 $ 108-148

■ **OPENING HOURS 营业时间**
Lunch 午膳 12:00-14:00 (L.O.)
Dinner 晚膳 18:00-22:30 (L.O.)

■ **ANNUAL AND WEEKLY CLOSING**
休息日期
Closed Sunday 周日休息

META

Innovative • Contemporary
创新菜•时尚

Sit at the black marble-topped counter to watch the chefs go about their business at this innovative, modern restaurant. The energetic Korean chef is a protégé of Tetsuya Wakuda and his cooking infuses European dishes with Korean and Asian notes; try the Korean-style seafood pancake. Dishes are refined and inventive and make good use of the ingredients; the seafood comes from various Asian countries while the meat is mostly from Australia.

餐厅大部分空间划为开放式厨房，食客可坐在黑色大理石餐桌前边用餐，边观赏厨房内的情形，趣味盎然。这里只供应厨师套餐，韩国主厨以现代欧陆烹调方法作基础，加入韩国元素，并选用来自韩国、亚洲和澳洲的时令食材，惊喜处处。附加餐单内的韩式海鲜煎薄饼传自主厨的祖母，值得一试。

NOURI N

Innovative • Elegant

创新菜 • 典雅

An eye-catching white marble table runs along the length of the dining room conjoining the chefs' counter where the magic happens. The main menu rotates on a seasonal basis and the innovative food comes with global influences – the 'bread and broth' (rye sourdough, silken cheese and vegetable broth) is unmissable. An excellent wine and sake list comes with an emphasis on natural wines and rare finds. Service is attentive and friendly.

餐厅名称的灵感来自Nourish一字，厨师寄意店子能成为一个"滋养"人际关系与成长的地方。餐厅布置细节都流露出这背后理念：开扬的开放式厨房让客人用餐时能同时欣赏厨艺及与厨师交流；侍应的服务亲切细心而毫不拘谨，处处令人感到自在放松。味蕾的感觉当然亦受照顾，餐厅定时轮替时令菜单，厨师以创新手法将新鲜食材入馔，其中自家制黑麦包配以精心熬制蔬菜汤及芝士豆腐酱更加不容错过。

10

TEL. 6221 4148

72 Amoy Street

厦门街72号

www.nouri.com.sg

■ **PRICE** 价钱

Lunch 午膳
set 套餐 $ 85-135
à la carte 点菜 $ 35-50
Dinner 晚膳
set 套餐 $ 140-240

■ **OPENING HOURS** 营业时间

Lunch 午膳 11:30-14:30 (L.O.)
Dinner 晚膳 18:00-22:30 (L.O.)

■ **ANNUAL AND WEEKLY CLOSING** 休息日期

Closed 4 days Lunar New Year, Monday lunch and Sunday
农历新年4天、周一午膳及周日休息

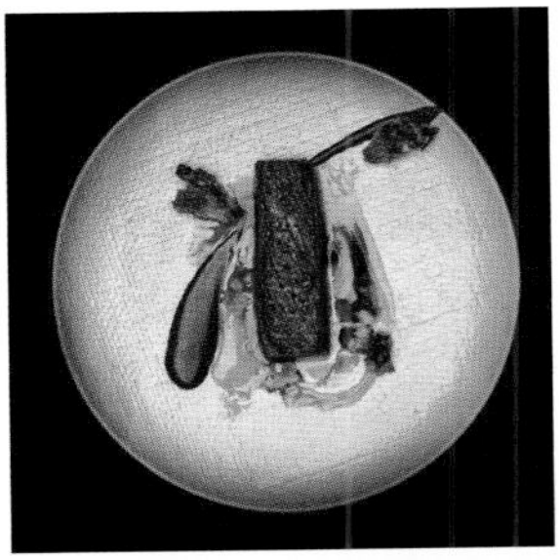
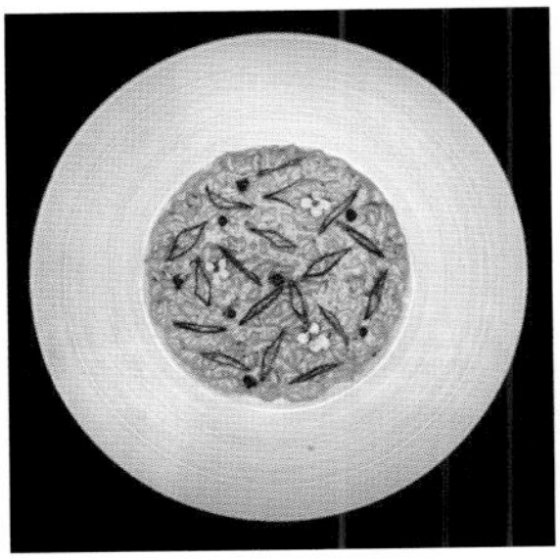
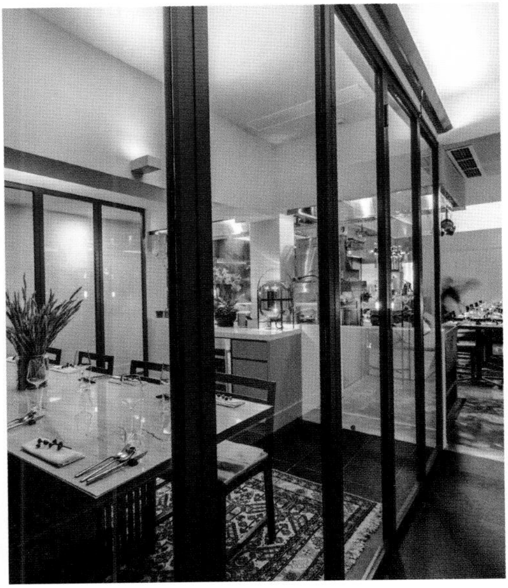

🍴14 🏨

TEL. 6295 6358

127-129 Kitchener Road
吉真那路127-129号

www.putien.com

■ **PRICE 价钱**
Lunch 午膳
à la carte 点菜 $ 30-50
Dinner 晚膳
à la carte 点菜 $ 30-50

■ **OPENING HOURS 营业时间**
Lunch 午膳 11:30-14:30 (L.O.)
Dinner 晚膳 17:30-22:00 (L.O.)

■ **ANNUAL AND WEEKLY CLOSING**
休息日期
Closed 1 day Lunar New Year
农历新年休息1天

CENTRAL 中区

❀

PUTIEN (KITCHENER ROAD)
莆田 (吉真那路)

Fujian • Simple
福建菜•简朴

Opened in 2000, this was the first branch of this chain known for its exceptionally friendly service. The updated dining room boasts a light-colour scheme and modern aesthetic. The signature seaweed with mini shrimps, available November-March, uses only the first harvest of Fujian seaweed for its nutritional value. From April-August, ask about the 6-cm-long razor clams straight from the restaurant's namesake city in Fujian.

这是集团的首家店子，早于2000年开业，2018年的翻新让餐厅换上了明亮而年青化的新装，而其以客为先并将最好献上的待客之道始终未变。招牌菜之一的虾苗拌紫菜只采用产自福建、首次收割的紫菜，因此只在十一月至三月限量供应。若在四至八月到访，则不要错过以莆田出产海蛏炮制的海蛏菜式。

RHUBARB

French contemporary • Classic

时尚法国菜•经典

Tranquil Duxton Hill is the setting for this smart French restaurant opened by two alumni of Au Petit Salut. Backed by their former employer, they have created an intimate spot with just seven tables and an open kitchen. The sophisticated cooking is deeply rooted in French classical cuisine but subtly and intelligently updated without recourse to gimmicks. To accompany the food is a thoughtfully compiled, predominantly French wine list.

因着大厨Paul Longworth对经典法国菜的热爱，也凭藉他的丰富经验和烹饪天赋，这儿供应的高级精致法国菜味道正宗、忠于传统之余，还有点不经意的现代风味。细腻的烹调功夫让食物味道的平衡与对比拿捏得恰到好处。葡萄大黄玫瑰乳鸽是此店名菜。悉心挑选过的法国红酒单内全是有名的法国佳酿。

⇔12 ☺🍴 ⅏

TEL. 8127 5001

3 Duxton Hill

达士敦山3号

www.rhubarb.sg

■ **PRICE** 价钱
Lunch 午膳
set 套餐 $ 48-78
à la carte 点菜 $ 75-125
Dinner 晚膳
set 套餐 $ 148
à la carte 点菜 $ 75-125

■ **OPENING HOURS** 营业时间
Lunch 午膳 12:00-14:15 (L.O.)
Dinner 晚膳 18:30-21:30 (L.O.)
Saturday dinner 周六晚膳
18:00-22:00 (L.O.)

■ **ANNUAL AND WEEKLY CLOSING**
休息日期
Closed Saturday lunch and Sunday
周六午膳及周日休息

CENTRAL 中区

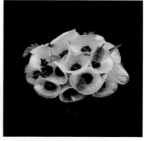

≮ **P** ⇔8 ◑¶ ⅏

TEL. 6438 0887

**One Fullerton, #02-02B,
1 Fullerton Road**
浮尔顿路1号浮尔顿一号#02-02B

www.saintpierre.com.sg

■ **PRICE 价钱**
Lunch 午膳
set 套餐 $ 58-100
à la carte 点菜 $ 130-230
Dinner 晚膳
set 套餐 $ 148-248
à la carte 点菜 $ 130-230

■ **OPENING HOURS 营业时间**
Lunch 午膳 11:30-14:00 (L.O.)
Dinner 晚膳 18:30-21:30 (L.O.)

■ **ANNUAL AND WEEKLY CLOSING**
休息日期
Closed Monday and Saturday lunch;
Sunday
周一、周六午膳及周日休息

SAINT PIERRE
French contemporary • Elegant
时尚法国菜•典雅

Not only does this smartly dressed restaurant offer great views of the marina, but its assured service and discreet atmosphere also make it a great choice for those on a date. The creative and contemporary French cuisine comes with pronounced Asian elements, with much of the produce sourced from Japan. There is a choice of three set menus: 'Classic', 'Discovery' and 'Prestige', all of which are available with wine pairings.

小小的餐室座位不多,好处是能让店东兼主厨更妥贴地照顾每桌客人和处理每一道菜肴。时尚且有水准的美馔以日本食材炮制而成,带有亚洲的烹调风味。餐厅有素食供应,但客人需主动向店家查询,此外,还有专为儿童而设的菜单。能远眺滨海湾金沙,景色优美,尤其是晚上,是浪漫约会必选之地。

SHINJI (BRAS BASAH ROAD)

Sushi • Classic

寿司·经典

Shinji Kanesaka's first outpost outside Japan relocated to the Carlton hotel following the revamping of Raffles. From the hinoki counter you can watch the same trusted team prepare the same high quality, traditional Edomae-style sushi. To make the most of the experience go for the omakase menu, although there are more affordable menu options available at lunchtime. Reservations are strongly recommended as it closes randomly according to fish supplies.

餐厅乃一贯传统江户风格设计，环境舒适，寿司套餐价格合理、水准上乘。坐在以原木切割而成的寿司枱可欣赏到厨师纯熟的手艺。推介午膳的雪/月/花套餐，各包括汤品、甜品和九至十五件寿司。生日在此聚餐时厨师和服务员更会为主人翁送上惊喜。因筑地市场及日本休假或令鱼类供应不足，餐厅会不定时休息，到访前宜先查询。

♿ 🅿 ⇔12 🍴 ◐¶

TEL. 6338 6131

Carlton Hotel, Lobby Level,
76 Bras Basah Road

勿拉士峇沙路76号
卡尔登酒店大堂楼层

www.shinjibykanesaka.com

■ PRICE 价钱
Lunch 午膳
set 套餐 $ 75-300
Dinner 晚膳
set 套餐 $ 220-500

■ OPENING HOURS 营业时间
Lunch 午膳 12:00-14:00 (L.O.)
Dinner 晚膳 18:00-21:00 (L.O.)

■ ANNUAL AND WEEKLY CLOSING
休息日期
Closed Tsukiji Market Holidays and
Sunday 筑地市场休息日及周日休息

CENTRAL 中区

CENTRAL 中区

 ♿ 🏊 🅿 🍽8 🚗 ◐▯

TEL. 6884 8239

The St. Regis Hotel, Lobby Level, 29 Tanglin Road

东陵路29号瑞吉酒店大堂楼层

www.shinjibykanesaka.com

■ **PRICE 价钱**
Lunch 午膳
set 套餐 $ 125-250
Dinner 晚膳
set 套餐 $ 220-450

■ **OPENING HOURS 营业时间**
Lunch 午膳 12:00-14:00 (L.O.)
Dinner 晚膳 18:00-21:00 (L.O.)

■ **ANNUAL AND WEEKLY CLOSING**
休息日期
Closed Sunday 周日休息

 🏵

SHINJI (TANGLIN ROAD)

Sushi · Classic

寿司·經典

The second restaurant under the aegis of celebrated Japanese chef Shinji Kanesaka is here on the lobby level of the St. Regis hotel. The entrance is typically discreet and leads into an intimate space with seating at the hinoki cypress counter for 18. Three set menus are offered – for a memorable experience the omakase is the best choice. The ingredients are as fresh as can be, with fish flown in from Tokyo's Tsukiji market.

全店装潢雅致朴素，只得十八个座位，食客可观摩厨师的精湛厨艺，食材由东京筑地市场新鲜运到。午膳和晚膳分别设三款套餐，只想吃寿司的话不妨点选有十五件寿司的江户前(Edomae)套餐，否则建议试试厨师发办套餐，会带来难以忘怀的味觉体验。

SUMMER PALACE
夏宫

Cantonese • Oriental décor

粤菜•东方

The Regent hotel's flagship restaurant is this authentic Cantonese restaurant which exudes a sense of calm and serenity. The signature dishes of the experienced head chef and his well-drilled kitchen include Five Spice deep-fried frog's legs; crispy roast pork; braised minced crabmeat in spinach soup; and fried chicken with almond flakes. The personable and professional service adds to the overall experience.

这中菜厅的装潢带浓浓中国色彩，金黄、大红等色调尽显富丽堂皇，宽敞的布置予食客宁静而舒适的用膳空间。这里由中国厨师主理，用料新鲜上乘，供应味道丰饶多姿的粤菜，招牌菜有酥炸田鸡腿、金牌脆皮烧肉、蟹肉菠菜羹及西柠杏香鸡等。

&♿ 🅿 ⊕60 ◑⊪

TEL. 6725 3288

Regent Hotel, Level 3,
1 Cuscaden Road

卡斯加登路1号丽晶酒店3层

www.regenthotels.com

■ **PRICE** 价钱
Lunch 午膳
set 套餐 $ 48-178
à la carte 点菜 $ 60-250
Dinner 晚膳
set 套餐 $ 76-178
à la carte 点菜 $ 60-250

■ **OPENING HOURS** 营业时间
Lunch 午膳 12:00-14:30 (L.O.)
Dinner 晚膳 18:30-22:30 (L.O.)

CENTRAL 中区

 🚻 ➰ 💺30 🕐🍴 ♨️

TEL. 6434 5286

**The Ritz-Carlton, Millenia, Level 3,
7 Raffles Avenue**

莱佛士道7号
丽思卡尔顿美年酒店3层

www.ritzcarlton.com

■ **PRICE** 价钱
Lunch 午膳
set 套餐 $ 58-178
à la carte 点菜 $ 60-200
Dinner 晚膳
set 套餐 $ 88-178
à la carte 点菜 $ 60-200

■ **OPENING HOURS** 营业时间
Lunch 午膳 11:30-14:15 (L.O.)
Dinner 晚膳 18:30-22:15 (L.O.)

SUMMER PAVILION
夏苑

Cantonese • Elegant
粤菜•典雅

The Chihuly lounge is a great place for a drink before you're ushered into the large, contemporary dining room surrounded by a garden. You'll be well looked after as the engaging staff provide service with plenty of vim and vigour. The extensive Cantonese menu covers all bases, with seafood a particular highlight; the double-boiled sea whelk soup with fish maw, poached rice with lobster and braised abalone are just some of the specialities.

偌大的餐室被现代中式庭园包围，延伸至天花的落地玻璃窗，触目所及均景色如画，特大的餐桌赋予客人更多空间，窗边位置尤佳，欲坐得亲密点，可选择半私人卡座。细致的绘瓷用具和充满活力的服务，特显豪华气派。菜单含括最典型的粤菜，招牌菜有椰皇花胶响螺炖鸡汤、龙虾西施泡饭和蚝皇四头南非鲍鱼。

SUSHI ICHI
鮨一

Sushi • Classic
寿司 • 经典

The silky smooth and tactile counter was fashioned from a 300-year-old cypress and the wooden ornaments on the wall were handmade by a famous carpenter in Nara. Traditional Edomae sushi is made with seasonal seafood and vegetables from Japan. Only the best rice, marinated with red or white vinegar, makes it to the counter. Even the sauces are shipped from their flagship store in Japan to maintain consistency. The omakase menu is recommended.

餐厅处处显细致——长十余尺的餐柜枱以超过三百年的柏木所造，墙上木饰出自奈良名匠手笔，更设系统记录客人喜好。厨师极注重寿司饭品质，只选用当时产量最佳之米种，按食材分别混和红醋或白醋，并时刻监控素质；时令海产、蔬菜皆由日本运到，酱汁亦由日本本店调制，以保持味道一致。推介厨师发办套餐。

🚉 📶🍴

TEL. 6235 5514
Marriott Tang Plaza Hotel,
#01-04, 320 Orchard Road
乌节路320号万豪董厦酒店#01-04
www.ginza-sushiichi.jp

■ **PRICE** 价钱
Lunch 午膳
set 套餐 $ 100-430
Dinner 晚膳
set 套餐 $ 220-430

■ **OPENING HOURS** 营业时间
Lunch 午膳 12:00-14:00 (L.O.)
Dinner 晚膳 18:00-21:30 (L.O.)

■ **ANNUAL AND WEEKLY CLOSING**
休息日期
Closed Monday 周一休息

CENTRAL 中区

CENTRAL 中区

P ⇔10 ⇷ ◎⑪

TEL. 6734 3520

**Palais Renaissance, #01-07,
390 Orchard Road**

乌节路390号文艺复兴广场#01-07

www.sushikimura.com.sg

■ **PRICE 价钱**
Lunch 午膳
set 套餐 $ 120-250
Dinner 晚膳
set 套餐 $ 280-400

■ **OPENING HOURS 营业时间**
Lunch 午膳 12:00-14:00 (L.O.)
Dinner 晚膳 19:00-21:00 (L.O.)

■ **ANNUAL AND WEEKLY CLOSING**
休息日期
Closed 5 days Japanese New Year,
4 days Lunar New Year and Monday
日本新年5天、农历新年4天及周一休
息

❀

SUSHI KIMURA
鮨来村

Sushi • Classic
寿司•经典

The owner-chef certainly pays attention to details: a hinoki counter crafted from one 150-year-old tree; organic sushi rice from one specific farm in Yamagata Prefecture cooked in Hokkaido spring water; and 100% of ingredients shipped from Japan. He excels in ageing raw fish in various ways, but the abalone cooked in sake for 8 hours deserves a mention. The rice bowl with uni, ikura, chopped toro and onsen tamago is rich, creamy and well-balanced.

"来村"意指欢迎来到厨师木村信男的餐厅中,而迎接着客人的,则是擅长对鲜鱼进行不同熟成技巧的主厨炮制的鲜味手握寿司。店内由布置到食材均注重呈现地道日本风味,150年原块扁柏木造的餐桌,以及全由日本进口的食材,甚至连米饭,也是厨师亲自向山形县农夫选购。招牌菜少不了主厨特别调配的小碗,混和海胆、三文鱼籽、鲔鱼及温泉蛋,既鲜味又口感丰盈,不容错过。

THE KITCHEN AT BACCHANALIA
Innovative • Contemporary
创新菜 • 时尚

The idea here is that there are no barriers between you and the chefs – and with an open kitchen on both sides there's no danger of that. The Australian-born head chef has an impressive international résumé and his contemporary cuisine uses plenty of modern techniques while ensuring that the quality of the ingredients really comes through. The restaurant's understated glass façade offers few hints as to what's happening inside.

开放式厨房，让厨师们在厨房内的工作情况一览无遗，令你能放胆开怀地品尝每道美食。在澳洲出生的主厨曾于英国和荷兰等地工作，丰富的厨房工作经验，使他的烹调风格也很国际化，以现代烹调技巧和元素处理的时尚菜式，完全展现出食材的原味与鲜味。

TEL. 9179 4552
39 Hong Kong Street
香港街39号
www.bacchanalia.asia

■ **PRICE** 价钱
Lunch 午膳
set 套餐 $ 65-145
Dinner 晚膳
set 套餐 $ 115-260

■ **OPENING HOURS** 营业时间
Lunch 午膳 12:00-14:30 (L.O.)
Dinner 晚膳 18:00-22:30 (L.O.)

■ **ANNUAL AND WEEKLY CLOSING**
休息日期
Closed Sunday and Monday
周日及周一休息

CENTRAL 中区

🏠 P ⇔12 ◑🍴

TEL. 6836 0055

33 Scotts Road

史各士路33号

www.thesongofindia.com

- **■ PRICE 价钱**
Lunch 午膳
set 套餐 $ 30-45
à la carte 点菜 $ 85-135
Dinner 晚膳
set 套餐 $ 79-220
à la carte 点菜 $ 85-135

- **■ OPENING HOURS 营业时间**
Lunch 午膳 12:00-14:30 (L.O.)
Dinner 晚膳 18:00-22:15 (L.O.)

CENTRAL 中区

THE SONG OF INDIA

Indian • Classic

印度菜 • 经典

You'll soon forget the less-than-convenient location as you climb the few steps of this period bungalow and get your first glimpse of the restaurant. The stylish interior and Indian artwork add to its appealing feel. The menu features delicacies from across India and the kitchen uses traditional methods of preparation alongside more modern cooking styles. The 'Song's Art Palette' allows you to try a number of dishes on a single platter. Try also 'flambé leg of lamb' which is prepared by the table.

餐厅位于一幢殖民时期独立大宅内,踏上梯级,推开大门,你会被餐室内雍容华贵的布置和墙上的精美挂画迷住。印度各地美食都可在这里的餐单上找到,主厨将现代元素融合到印度传统烹调上,Song's Art Palette套餐可一次过品尝多款特色印度小菜,席前预备的火焰羊腿则是主厨的新创作。

WHITEGRASS

Australian contemporary • Elegant

时尚澳洲菜 • 典雅

This charming restaurant is set in the second oldest building in Singapore, formerly a school run by nuns. The vibrant homely décor and fresh flowers set nicely against the modern dishes created by the Australian owner-chef that showcase an elegant and delicate mix of complementing flavours. Desserts, like coconut mousse with jackfruit ice cream, are a highlight. The small but well-chosen wine list focuses on Italian and Australian estates.

前身是学校，又是新加坡第二古老的建筑物，在此文化底蕴中营运的餐厅，自然散发出引人入胜的高雅。具殖民时期风格的外观以及明亮典雅的私人厢房予人愉悦的用餐体验。澳洲或日本等地进口的食材在巧妙技巧下成为一道道精致时尚的佳肴，晚餐菜单更能体会到厨师于烹调上的野心，甜品别出心裁，椰子慕斯配以菠萝蜜冰淇淋值得一试。

P ⇌30 ⊙¶

TEL. 6837 0402

**Chijmes, #01-26/27,
30 Victoria Street**

維多利亞街30号
赞美广场#01-26/27
www.whitegrass.com.sg

■ **PRICE** 价钱
Lunch 午膳
set 套餐 $ 70-230
Dinner 晚膳
set 套餐 $ 116-265

■ **OPENING HOURS** 营业时间
Lunch 午膳 12:00-14:30 (L.O.)
Dinner 晚膳 18:00-21:30 (L.O.)

■ **ANNUAL AND WEEKLY CLOSING**
休息日期
Closed Tuesday lunch, Sunday and Monday 周二午膳、周日及周一休息

CENTRAL 中区

CENTRAL 中区

& 余 ⇔36 ⓞ
TEL. 6444 9672
165 Tanjong Pagar Road
丹戎巴葛路165号
www.bar-roque.com.sg

■ **PRICE 价钱**
Lunch 午膳
set 套餐 $ 38
à la carte 点菜 $ 45-110
Dinner 晚膳
set 套餐 $ 118
à la carte 点菜 $ 45-110

■ **OPENING HOURS 营业时间**
Lunch 午膳 12:00-14:30 (L.O.)
Dinner 晚膳 18:00-22:30 (L.O.)

■ **ANNUAL AND WEEKLY CLOSING**
休息日期
Closed Saturday lunch and Sunday
周六午膳及周日休息

BAR-ROQUE GRILL

European • Cosy
欧陆菜 • 舒适

Alsace-born Chef Stephane has created an appealing menu full of hearteningly satisfying dishes. He uses ingredients from all parts of the globe for his modern European cooking – something not to be missed is the rotisserie free-range chicken, which is from Malaysia. If you like sharing, also consider ordering the considerable 'beef platter' for your group. The room is warm and welcoming, if not quite as ornate as the punning name suggests.

甫走进餐馆内，热情好客的侍应生便主动前来招呼。深棕色家具、暗红色墙身、油画，为这家开业五年的餐厅添上历史意味。高级食材来自世界各地，供应的鸡肉，是由马来西亚引入、原籍法国的走地鸡，地理上的便利令鸡肉更新鲜，厨师悉心的烹调，令鸡肉的味道极致提升。自家制的烟熏食物也值得一尝。

KA SOH (OUTRAM PARK)
家嫂（欧南园）

Singaporean · Neighbourhood
新加坡菜·亲切

The location is a little unusual but then there's nothing like being surrounded by hospital buildings to remind you of the importance of a good diet. Order the famous speciality here of milky white fish soup with noodles – made by cooking fresh snakehead fish and fish bones for over 4 hours – and you'll feel instantly invigorated. The fried shrimp paste chicken is also worth trying. Ka Soh also has branches in Malaysia and Indonesia.

餐厅位于一幢两层高建筑内，同址有医生会所，四周则是医院建筑群。大厨是土生华人，炮制具本地色彩的潮、粤菜式，其中鱼汤米线不能错过，汤底以鲜鱼骨、生鱼熬制四小时，乳白鲜甜。虾酱鸡也十分惹味。鲜鱼可以选择以粤式、潮式或娘惹方式烹煮。餐厅在马来西亚和印尼都有分店。

P ◎↑

TEL. 6473 6686
2 College Road
学院路2号
www.ka-soh.com.sg

■ **PRICE** 价钱
Lunch 午膳
à la carte 点菜 $ 20-30
Dinner 晚膳
à la carte 点菜 $ 20-30

■ **OPENING HOURS** 营业时间
Lunch 午膳 11:30-14:30 (L.O.)
Dinner 晚膳 17:30-21:30 (L.O.)

CENTRAL 中区

CENTRAL 中区

🔲 Ⓢ 🚫🍴

TEL. 6223 2005

30-32 Keong Saik Road

恭锡路30-32号

■ **PRICE** 价钱

Lunch 午膳
à la carte 点菜 $ 15-25
Dinner 晚膳
à la carte 点菜 $ 15-25

■ **OPENING HOURS** 营业时间

Lunch 午膳 12:00-14:15 (L.O.)
Dinner 晚膳 17:00-22:30 (L.O.)

■ **ANNUAL AND WEEKLY CLOSING**
休息日期

Closed 7 days after Lunar New Year
and alternate Mondays
农历新年后7天及周一不定期休息

😊

KOK SEN
国成球记

Singaporean • Simple
新加坡菜 • 简朴

There's always a queue outside this simple coffee shop – join it and hope those already inside are quick eaters. The Wong family have been serving classic Cze Char dishes like seafood, eggplant and tofu claypot or curry fish tail at various addresses for nearly 50 years – hopefully the 3rd generation of the family will keep things going here for many more years to come. It's run with impressive efficiency, the food is tasty and the prices are friendly. Reservation is available for tables of six or above.

这里的煮炒菜式十分驰名,店外总有长长的人龙,你只能期待店内的食客快点吃完让座。东主以家族方式经营餐馆接近半世纪,曾先后迁至不同地址,现在由第三代经营。店内布置简单,食物价格相宜且非常滋味。初次光临的食客可在款式多元的餐牌上按图片点菜,咖喱鱼头或巧手三宝煲也值得一试。六位以上可订座。

LAGNAA

Indian • Exotic décor
印度菜 • 异国风情

You always have the final say on the level of spiciness of any dish you order at this three-storey restaurant in Little India, though many come for the Chilli Challenge on full moon nights to push their limits (The record currently stands at level 9). The owner-chef tries to include sweet, sour, salty, spicy, bitter and astringent flavours. His monthly specials feature seasonal ingredients and most dishes come in single serving sizes.

在印度商店林立的小印度区可找到这家供应南、北印度美食的餐厅，菜式全是现点现煮，且包含了印度菜应有的甜、酸、咸、辣、苦、涩六种味道，更设每月特别餐单。餐厅体贴地设有不同的辛辣度供选择，且提供一人分量菜式，单独用膳亦能大快朵颐。楼高三层的餐室布置简洁，每逢月圆之夜更会举行有趣的辣椒挑战，测试食客的耐辣程度。

⇪15 ◐🍴

TEL. 6296 1215
6 Upper Dickson Road
狄生路上段6号
www.lagnaa.com

■ **PRICE** 价钱
à la carte 点菜 $ 30-50

■ **OPENING HOURS** 营业时间
11:30-22:00 (L.O.)

■ **ANNUAL AND WEEKLY CLOSING**
休息日期
Closed 4 days Hari Raya Aidilfitri
开斋节休息4天

CENTRAL 中区

TEL. N/A

78 Smith Street
史密斯街78号

■ **PRICE** 价钱
à la carte 点菜 $ 5-15

■ **OPENING HOURS** 营业时间
10:00-20:00 (L.O.)

■ **ANNUAL AND WEEKLY CLOSING**
休息日期
Closed Wednesday 周三休息

CENTRAL 中区

LIAO FAN HAWKER CHAN
了凡香港油鸡饭·面
Cantonese Roast Meats · Simple
烧味·简朴

What started at a stall in Chinatown Food Centre lead inevitably to Chef Chan going into partnership and opening a restaurant. Equally inevitable is the size of the queue – it forms well before opening time, such is the reputation of his delicious soy sauce chicken rice and roast pork. The new premises may provide more space and seating but, just like back at the hawker centre, you'll be sharing your table with others.

还没到营业时间,已见长长的人龙在门外等候,为的只是一尝简单而味美的油鸡和烧味。主厨兼店东之一的陈先生继其在熟食小贩中心的小店后,开设了这家同样以油鸡和烧味作卖点的餐馆,这儿有空调系统且座位更多,虽仍要拼桌,但食客只为了食物的素质而来,因此一点也不在意。

MAN MAN (TANJONG PAGAR)
鳗满 (丹戎巴葛)

Japanese • Simple
日本菜 • 简朴

The live eels are flown in from Japan's Aichi Prefecture. They are then cleaned and gutted in the glass-fronted kitchen before being grilled over a charcoal pit – it's quite a performance to watch. They arrive at your table crispy on the outside and soft and yielding on the inside – and are made even more delicious thanks to the accompanying secret sauce. No bookings are taken so it's worth arriving early.

门前的小牌匾虽不显眼，但香浓的炭烤味早已飘散于空气中，引来不少老饕在门外轮候。进门后迎来的是一个神秘鱼池，内里养着爱知县进口的鳗鱼，旁边是主厨工作的半开放式厨房，欲一睹主厨烹调鳗鱼的过程，务必要求厨房前的座位。除了香口软熟带油香的新鲜鳗鱼外，必要点选店长推介的限定品烧鳗鱼肝。

TEL. 6222 0678
#01-01, 1 Keong Saik Road
恭锡路1号#01-01

■ **PRICE** 价钱
Lunch 午膳
set 套餐 $ 21-72
à la carte 点菜 $ 35-65
Dinner 晚膳
set 套餐 $ 21-72
à la carte 点菜 $ 35-65

■ **OPENING HOURS** 营业时间
Lunch 午膳 11:30-14:30 (L.O.)
Dinner 晚膳 18:00-22:00 (L.O.)

■ **ANNUAL AND WEEKLY CLOSING**
休息日期
Closed 10 days Lunar New Year and Sunday 农历新年10天及周日休息

CENTRAL 中区

CENTRAL 中区

 ♿ 🛋 ⃝||

TEL. 6392 1722

#01-01, 138 Race Course Road
跑马埔路138号#01-01
www.muthuscurry.com

■ **PRICE** 价钱
à la carte 点菜 $ 20-25

■ **OPENING HOURS** 营业时间
10:30-22:30 (L.O.)

MUTHU'S CURRY (LITTLE INDIA) N

Indian · Colourful
印度菜·亮丽

'Muthu' means pearl in Tamil, befitting this gem with three other branches serving traditional south Indian cuisine from the Chettinad region. Originally called Muthu's Makan shop, the owner expanded and renamed it in 1982. The signature dish is the fish head curry, made using a secret blend of spices. Flower crab, masala prawns and tandoori chicken are also big hits among diners.

由小店开始，这家主营南印度传统菜式的餐厅在本地坐拥三家店子。名称Muthu在坦米尔语中有珍珠之意，而餐厅的珍宝则非其招牌菜咖喱鱼头莫属，菜式配方只由店东两兄弟持有，保证只此一家。作为经营三十多年的店子，拿手菜当然不绝于此，花蟹、马沙拉虾及天都里鸡皆深受客人爱戴。

SONG FA BAK KUT TEH (NEW BRIDGE ROAD)
松發肉骨茶 (新桥路)

Singaporean • Simple
新加坡菜 • 简朴

Much has changed since Mr Yeo started selling bak kut teh from his pushcart in Johor Road back in the late '60s – nowadays it's the second generation of the family who are running the show. They are still selling their celebrated pork ribs and peppery broth but are now doing so from 5 shops – and this one, the simplest, seems to be the best. Queue, order, pay, and then tuck into your soup – when you've finished they'll top it up for you.

创办人杨先生曾是街头小贩,从1969年起,伴他走过数十载、让他养活妻儿的,就是一辆木头车和一碗香喷喷热腾腾的肉骨茶。从木头车到店铺,松發肉骨茶也是我们的共同回忆,现在由杨氏长子继承,卖的仍然是为人熟悉的肉骨茶和同样美味的鱼汤。店内常常座无虚席,欲寻找回忆中的味道,便要乖乖排队候座。

✍️🍴

TEL. 6533 6128
#01-01, 11 New Bridge Road
新桥路11号#01-01
www.songfa.com.sg

■ **PRICE** 价钱
à la carte 点菜 $ 10-20

■ **OPENING HOURS** 营业时间
09:00-21:15 (L.O.)

■ **ANNUAL AND WEEKLY CLOSING**
休息日期
Closed 3 days Lunar New Year and Monday 农历新年3天及周一休息

CENTRAL 中区

⊕ 50 ☺️⏏️

TEL. 6222 3928
97 Tanjong Pagar Road
丹戎巴葛路97号
www.theblueginger.com

■ **PRICE** 价钱
Lunch 午膳
à la carte 点菜 $ 20-65
Dinner 晚膳
à la carte 点菜 $ 20-65

■ **OPENING HOURS** 营业时间
Lunch 午膳 12:00-14:15 (L.O.)
Dinner 晚膳 18:30-21:45 (L.O.)

■ **ANNUAL AND WEEKLY CLOSING**
休息日期
Closed 3 days Lunar New Year
农历新年休息3天

THE BLUE GINGER

Peranakan • Traditional
娘惹菜 • 传统

There is no shortage of cute little places in Chinatown – this is one of the more popular and it's easy to see why. The narrow house offers dining on three of its floors and the works of local artists are used to add colour and character. The aromatic cuisine delivers all the subtle and authentic flavours of Peranakan – and the reason its regulars keep returning is that the portions are as generous as the prices.

在行人络绎不绝的牛车水内一条长长的街道上，不难发现这家以红色和巨型招牌作招徕的餐馆，细小的空间只有数张小桌子，以本地油画装饰，缤纷的色彩中带着独特的韵味。阿参、参巴辣椒、姜花等，大量的马来和印尼香料混合出浓烈的酸辣香气。每小碟菜式，都是有素质及味道正宗的娘惹菜。

THE COCONUT CLUB
椰子俱乐部

Malaysian • Friendly
马来西亚菜 • 友善

The emphasis here is on making everything from scratch and not just the coconut milk and sambal sauce. It offers traditional fare that may seem easy but is meticulously made. As its name suggests, coconut plays a big part on the menu and only the Malaysian Mewe variety is used. The famous nasi lemak ayam goreng berempah exudes a light coconut fragrance. Finish your meal with cendol or traditional kuih muih. Service from the energetic team is friendly and attentive.

东主期盼将最传统的马来西亚口味带给食客。诚如其名,椰子乃菜式中的灵魂,秉持原汁原味,选用的椰子也是从马来西亚入口。菜式看似随性简单,唯每步均由厨房制作;鲜榨椰奶、秘制参巴酱,全是满满的心机。招牌菜有沁出淡淡椰香的炸鸡腿椰浆饭,珍多冰更是必试甜品。绘有水岸小屋的墙为餐厅倍添怀旧马国风情。

🚊 🅿️🍴

TEL. 6635 2999
6 Ann Siang Hill
安祥山6号
www.thecoconutclub.sg

■ **PRICE** 价钱
Lunch 午膳
à la carte 点菜 $ 15-25
Dinner 晚膳
à la carte 点菜 $ 15-25

■ **OPENING HOURS** 营业时间
Lunch 午膳 11:00-14:45 (L.O.)
Dinner 晚膳 18:00-21:30 (L.O.)

■ **ANNUAL AND WEEKLY CLOSING**
休息日期
Closed 2 days New Year, 4 days Lunar New Year, 4 days Hari Raya Aidilfitri, 2 days Christmas and New Year eve
新年2天、农历新年4天、开斋节4天、圣诞2天及除夕休息

CENTRAL 中区

P 🪑12 ⛓ ◐🍴

TEL. 6836 5680

**Robertson Walk, #01-02,
11 Unity Street**
团结街11号罗拔申廊#01-02

■ **PRICE** 价钱
Dinner 晚膳
set 套餐 $ 27-39
à la carte 点菜 $ 35-60

■ **OPENING HOURS** 营业时间
Dinner 晚膳 18:00-22:00 (L.O.)

■ **ANNUAL AND WEEKLY CLOSING**
休息日期
Closed Sunday 周日休息

TORITAMA SHIROKANE
酉玉白金

Japanese • Simple
日本菜 • 简朴

If you're looking for authentic yakitori then this outpost of the Tokyo-based Toritama group is the place to come. The appetite-enhancing aromas hit you as soon as you enter the room. There are 20+ chicken parts to choose from, so the more adventurous eater will find much to excite them. The skewers are grilled over charcoal in the open kitchen in front of the customers, although you're protected from the cooking by a glass shield.

装潢富现代气息，开放式烧烤厨房设在餐厅中央，烤炉与吧座之间有玻璃相间，阻隔了油烟。餐厅提供正宗日式烧鸡串，可选择鸡皮、不同部位的鸡肉、内脏，以至牛、猪等肉食及日本蔬菜，厨师即席以炭火烤制，香气扑鼻，适合亲友聚会。

TRUE BLUE CUISINE
Peranakan · Traditional
娘惹菜·传统

It's less like walking into a restaurant, more like falling into the warm embrace of a much loved family member. Here it's about nostalgia and paying homage to the food, history and customs of the Peranakans – you'll find all the classic dishes, prepared in an authentic way, and the hard part is narrowing down your choice. The setting really is unique and on the way out it's hard to resist buying a keepsake from the True Blue Shoppe.

创办人兼主厨Benjamin Seck指这儿是活的遗产，餐厅内布置大量怀旧娘惹古董，气氛陈旧，仿如置身某家庭的饭厅之中。作为狮城其中一家历史最长的娘惹餐厅，餐单上是数之不尽的传统菜式，选菜可能会费尽脑力。尝过美味的菜肴，不妨逛逛餐厅外的博物馆和商店，体会浓浓的娘惹风情。

🍴14 🕙

TEL. 6440 0449
47/49 Armenian Street
亚米尼亚街47/49号
www.truebluecuisine.com

■ PRICE 价钱
Lunch 午膳
set 套餐 $ 32
à la carte 点菜 $ 40-100
Dinner 晚膳
set 套餐 $ 42
à la carte 点菜 $ 40-100

■ OPENING HOURS 营业时间
Lunch 午膳 11:30-14:00 (L.O.)
Dinner 晚膳 18:00-21:00 (L.O.)

CENTRAL 中区

75

☎🍴

TEL. 6221 6583

76 Peck Seah Street

柏城街76号

www.wholeearth.com.sg

■ **PRICE 价钱**
Lunch 午膳
à la carte 点菜 $ 30-45
Dinner 晚膳
à la carte 点菜 $ 30-45

■ **OPENING HOURS 营业时间**
Lunch 午膳 11:30-14:30 (L.O.)
Dinner 晚膳 17:30-21:15 (L.O.)

WHOLE EARTH
環界

Vegetarian • Simple
素菜 • 简朴

"Vegetarian cuisine for non-vegetarians" is how Phyllis and Wood describe their longstanding Thai and Peranakan restaurant. They wanted diners to feel they were eating meat even though they weren't and this they achieve through an understanding of textures and flavours and the clever use of soy product and tofu. With dishes like Tom Yam soup and classic Assam Pedas, the food is full of flavour as well as being good for you – and it's great value too.

给无肉不欢者的素食,是店主和经理对餐馆的形容。为了让味道较清淡的豆腐和豆类制品变得惹味可口,餐厅选用泰国和娘惹菜的烹调方法炮制风格独特的健康素菜,如泰式的南泰东炎汤味道浓烈鲜明、经典娘惹菜阿参鱼,质感与肉类无异,啖啖素鱼肉,非常滋味。新装修过的餐室以蓝色为主调,使用餐气氛更添平静。

YHINGTHAI PALACE
銀泰

Thai · Exotic décor
泰国菜 · 异国风情

Founded in the '90s by a couple passionate about Thai cuisine, this restaurant is spread over three colourful rooms decorated with Thai artefacts. Added authenticity comes courtesy of the helpful waitresses in their delightful traditional dress. The Thai and Thai-Chinese dishes are prepared with obvious care, with choices like Thai Otah. Prices are reasonable, both for this neighbourhood and for the quality of the food.

女店东曾于泰国工作多年，夫妇二人对泰国菜均情有独锺。此店供应正宗和混合了中式口味的泰国菜。鲜芒果沙拉、蒸鱼饼、青咖喱鸡是此店名菜。泰式艺术摆设及穿着传统泰式服装的女服务员在店内穿梭往来，将菜式奉送到客人面前，满有泰国风情。具素质的食物和相宜的价钱，是不错的用餐选择。

TEL. 6337 1161
#01-04, 36 Purvis Street
巴米士街36号#01-04
www.yhingthai.com.sg

■ **PRICE** 价钱
Lunch 午膳
à la carte 点菜 $ 35-50
Dinner 晚膳
à la carte 点菜 $ 45-60

■ **OPENING HOURS** 营业时间
Lunch 午膳 11:30-13:45 (L.O.)
Dinner 晚膳 18:00-21:30 (L.O.)

CENTRAL 中区

CENTRAL 中区

🍴◐❚

TEL. 6818 1914

JW Marriott Hotel South Beach,
Level B1M, South Tower,
30 Beach Road

美芝路30号万豪南岸酒店
南翼B1M层

www.akiraback.com

■ **PRICE 价钱**
Lunch 午膳
set 套餐 $ 35-55
à la carte 点菜 $ 65-140
Dinner 晚膳
à la carte 点菜 $ 65-140

■ **OPENING HOURS 营业时间**
Lunch 午膳 12:00-14:30 (L.O.)
Dinner 晚膳 18:00-21:30 (L.O.)

🍴

AKIRA BACK

Innovative · Chic
创新菜·新潮

Named after the chef himself and decorated
with his mother's paintings, it champions a
communal dining concept with dishes meant
for sharing among friends. The menu shows
strong Korean and Japanese influences, while
ingredients are flown in from around the world.
His specialities include AB pizza, AB tacos,
'Perfect Storm', and 'Brother from Another
Mother'. Sake lovers should try Nanbu Bijin,
exclusively available here.

Akira锐意於此店呈现其烹调理念和特色;不但亲自
挑选及培训厨房内的每一个人员,更特意于餐厅挂上
了母亲的画作。店内运用世界各地的食材炮制出具日
韩风味的菜式,除了招牌菜AB比萨、AB玉米饼及卷
物(Perfect Storm)等,也会按季节推出特有的时令
菜式,店内更提供其家族酿酒厂酿造的清酒南部美人
(Nanbu Bijin)。

ANGLO INDIAN (SHENTON WAY)

Indian • Simple
印度菜•简朴

If there's one dish that customers should expect to find in a restaurant called Anglo Indian it's chicken tikka masala – and sure enough it's a firm favourite of many here at this simply decorated spot in the heart of the CBD. The dining room may seat only 20 but there's a large outdoor terrace where everyone congregates for the well-priced cooking. Other popular choices include butter chicken and lamb dum biryani.

位于中心商业区且就在珊顿壹号楼下，布置简单，以黑白旧照片点缀的餐室内只有二十个座位，然而宽敞的户外座位完全弥补了不足。小小的厨房只以一道大玻璃窗与餐室区分开来，食客能欣赏厨师工作时的风采。马萨拉鸡、牛油鸡及烤羊肉印度香米是招牌菜。

TEL. 6636 9411
#01-08, 1 Shenton Way
珊顿大道1号#01-08
www.angloindiancafebar.com

■ **PRICE** 价钱
Lunch 午膳
set 套餐 $ 24
à la carte 点菜 $ 25-70
Dinner 晚膳
à la carte 点菜 $ 25-70

■ **OPENING HOURS** 营业时间
11:00-22:00 (L.O.)

CENTRAL 中区

♿ 🅿 🚻40 🚗 ⊘🍴

TEL. 6825 1008

InterContinental Hotel, Level 1, 80 Middle Road

密驼路80号洲际酒店地面层

ashandelm.sg

■ **PRICE 价钱**
Lunch 午膳
set 套餐 $ 28-138
à la carte 点菜 $ 40-250
Dinner 晚膳
set 套餐 $ 10-168
à la carte 点菜 $ 40-250

■ **OPENING HOURS 营业时间**
Lunch 午膳 12:00-14:30 (L.O.)
Dinner 晚膳 18:00-22:00 (L.O.)

🍽○

ASH & ELM

European • Fashionable

欧陆菜 • 时髦

There aren't many restaurants that are as good at hosting business lunches as they are for entertaining large family tables, but then this restaurant, within the InterContinental hotel, is unlike most. It serves a mix of dishes from across Europe, from three kitchens: one for cheese and charcuterie, one for wood-fired dishes and one for charcoal-grilled meats. The high ceiling adds grandeur to the large, contemporary and thoughtfully-lit room.

高高的天花、时尚舒适的布置、柔和温暖的灯光和开放式厨房，建构出温馨写意的空间。餐馆供应混合了法国、意大利、西班牙等欧洲各地风味和扒房概念的菜式。在这儿，你可以品尝到来自欧洲各国的冻肉、法式蛋黄酱拌蟹饼、凯撒沙拉、碳火烤肉、精选乳酪等等。

AURA

Italian • Elegant
意大利菜 • 典雅

If nourishment is needed after a contemplative tour of the National Gallery, then Aura and its breezy Sky Lounge sister are right on hand. Beppe de Vito and co have gathered together a seasoned team who understand the concept of hospitality and who deliver eminently satisfying Italian dishes like trofie with crab and porcini, scallops crudo with avocado and truffles, and grilled sea bream with pistachio salsa.

亲切专业的服务。装潢时尚高雅，长长的巨幅落地玻璃窗，街上景色尽收眼帘。烹饪团队由数位意大利厨师组成，为食客烹调美味的意大利菜。香菌蟹肉特飞面、松露鳄梨带子，光想想便已让人食指大动。精心挑选的葡萄酒单带给你意外惊喜。

♿ 🚌 ✂ 🅿 ⇔168 🍽 ⌗
TEL. 6866 1977
National Gallery Singapore, #05-03 and #06-02, 1 St. Andrews Road
圣安德烈路1号
国家美术馆#05-03、#06-02
www.aura.sg

■ **PRICE 价钱**
Lunch 午膳
set 套餐 $ 35-48
à la carte 点菜 $ 75-110
Dinner 晚膳
set 套餐 $ 108
à la carte 点菜 $ 75-110

■ **OPENING HOURS 营业时间**
Lunch 午膳 12:00-14:00 (L.O.)
Dinner 晚膳 18:30-22:00 (L.O.)

CENTRAL 中区

CENTRAL 中区

🏠 🅿 💺14 🍴 ⓘ🍴

TEL. 6226 0500

38-40 Tras Street
道拉实街38-40号

www.bam.sg

■ **PRICE 价钱**
Lunch 午膳
set 套餐 $ 40-98
Dinner 晚膳
set 套餐 $ 98-188

■ **OPENING HOURS 营业时间**
Lunch 午膳 12:00-13:45 (L.O.)
Dinner 晚膳 18:00-22:00 (L.O.)

■ **ANNUAL AND WEEKLY CLOSING**
休息日期
Closed Monday, Saturday & Public
Holidays lunch; 6 days Lunar New
Year and Sunday
周一、周六及公众假期午膳；农历新
年6天及周日休息

🍴◯

BAM!

Innovative • Design
创新菜•型格

Standing out from the crowd is never easy so
sometimes you have to try something unusual.
What makes this counter eatery so different is
in its pairing of Spanish and Japanese cuisines
to create an innovative and original style of
tapas and one designed to be enjoyed with
sake. They have over 80 different types of sake,
with a team trained to recommend the perfect
one. A renovation of the chic, understated
space left it with a little more room.

装潢简约西化，感觉随意、气氛轻松，最独特之处是
以日本清酒搭配西班牙美食。这里供应逾八十款清
酒，经训练的团队会为食客搭配最完美的清酒美食。
厨师以优质的食材、结合西班牙与日本最优秀的烹调
风格，创作出来的创新菜，甚有个人特色。

BISTRO DU VIN (SHAW CENTRE)

French • Bistro

法国菜•法式小餐馆

There are times when nothing hits the spot quite like classic Gallic cuisine, especially when it's being served in an archetypal bistro setting. Part of Les Amis restaurant group, this simple, unpretentious spot comes complete with vintage billboards; it's also quite small so it's best to book. Everyone will find their favourite here, whether that's soupe à l'oignon, charcuterie, steak frites, tarte aux pommes or soufflé au Grand Marnier.

Les Amis餐饮集团旗下一员，经典的法国小餐馆，每道菜都经厨师用心炮制：冻肉、鹅肝、洋葱汤、法式烤鸡、红酒汁炖牛面颊、牛排薯条、柑曼治橙酒梳乎厘等，菜式简单直接、不取巧却味美。典型的法国小餐馆布置：油画、法国佳酿广告照，充满法式风情。餐厅座位不多，建议预先订座。

TEL. 6733 7763

Shaw Centre, #01-14, 1 Scotts Road
史各士路1号邵氏中心#01-14
www.bistroduvin.com.sg

■ **PRICE** 价钱
Lunch 午膳
set 套餐 $ 34-60
à la carte 点菜 $ 60-170
Dinner 晚膳
à la carte 点菜 $ 60-170

■ **OPENING HOURS** 营业时间
Lunch 午膳 12:00-14:00 (L.O.)
Dinner 晚膳 18:30-22:00 (L.O.)

CENTRAL 中区

⊗🍴

TEL. 6254 3937

399, 401 & 403 Balestier Road
马里士他路399、401及403号

■ **PRICE** 价钱
Lunch 午膳
à la carte 点菜 $ 10-20
Dinner 晚膳
à la carte 点菜 $ 10-20

■ **OPENING HOURS** 营业时间
Lunch 午膳 11:00-16:30 (L.O.)
Dinner 晚膳 17:30-03:45 (L.O.)

🍴◯

BOON TONG KEE (BALESTIER ROAD)
文東記 (马里士他路)

Singaporean · Simple
新加坡菜·简朴

What started with a small stall is now a group of eight restaurants – this two-storey operation with a large kitchen was the first branch to open and has been going for nearly 40 years. At the beginning it just offered chicken rice, fish head and deep-fried tofu but now it provides a variety of Cze Char dishes. Singaporeans know their chicken and they know that this is the place to come for it.

文東記的鸡饭在本地久负盛名，由最初的小摊档发展到现在共有八间店子，这家位于马里士他路的是首家店铺、在四十年前开业，起初店面面积和厨房都很细小，只供应鸡饭、鱼头和炸豆腐，慢慢发展成为现在占地两层的餐馆并设有大型厨房，为食客提供更多煮炒菜式。风味地道的海南鸡值得一试。

BRASSERIE GAVROCHE

French • Bistro
法国菜•法式小餐馆

You won't just find Francophiles and homesick émigrés at this lively and atmospheric brasserie – it's the perfect spot for anyone after a 'little piece of France' in the city. The double doors and the antique wooden bar were both brought over from Paris and the chef-owner uses recipes for the classic dishes handed down to him by his grandfather. The wine list is a labour of love; try resisting some of its wonderful burgundies.

推开从巴黎运送过来的大门，屋内布置融合了法式小酒馆与啤酒馆风格，古董酒瓶冷却器、挂满一墙的法国旧照，是地道的法国风情。法式蜗牛、洋葱汤、鞑靼牛肉、牛排薯条等，全是法国菜经典，食谱承传自主厨的祖父。请预留位置品尝反烤苹果挞或拿破仑蛋糕。来自勃艮第酒区的优质餐酒令人难以抗拒。

TEL. 6225 8266
66 Tras Street
道拉实街66号
www.brasseriegavroche.com

■ **PRICE** 价钱
Lunch 午膳
à la carte 点菜 $ 65-105
Dinner 晚膳
à la carte 点菜 $ 65-105

■ **OPENING HOURS** 营业时间
Lunch 午膳 12:00-14:00 (L.O.)
Dinner 晚膳 18:30-21:30 (L.O.)

■ **ANNUAL AND WEEKLY CLOSING**
休息日期
Closed Sunday 周日休息

CENTRAL 中区

♿ 🚆 ⚲🍴

TEL. 6324 6225

126 Tanjong Pagar Road
丹戎巴葛路126号
www.bukonero.com.sg

■ **PRICE** 价钱
Lunch 午膳
set 套餐 $ 30-80
à la carte 点菜 $ 55-90
Dinner 晚膳
set 套餐 $ 90-125
à la carte 点菜 $ 55-90

■ **OPENING HOURS** 营业时间
Lunch 午膳 12:00-14:30 (L.O.)
Dinner 晚膳 18:30-22:00 (L.O.)

■ **ANNUAL AND WEEKLY CLOSING**
休息日期
Closed Tuesday & Wednesday
lunch; Sunday and Monday
周二及周三午膳；周日及周一休息

🍴🍽

BUKO NERO

Italian · Quirky
意大利菜·破格

There's rarely a spare seat to be had at this little neighbourhood spot and it's easy to understand why: Tracy is a bubbly, charming hostess and Oscar's food is carefully executed and has an innate simplicity that relies on the quality of the ingredients. Originally from Veneto, his style is informed by his travels; with Asian elements adding freshness to the Italian dishes. Don't miss the porcini soup, the spaghetti with crab and the gelato.

来自威尼托的主厨，烹调风格受到其游历和曾于多个亚洲国家工作的经验影响，带点亚洲风味。店内全部食品均是自家制作。上乘的食材，加上厨师的细心处理，呈给客人的意大利菜清新可口，讨人欢心。不要错过牛肝菌汤、蟹肉意大利面条和自制意大利冰淇淋。餐厅有提供套餐，需主动向店家取阅。

BUONA TERRA

Italian • Cosy
意大利菜 • 舒适

The entrance to this sophisticated and intimate Italian restaurant, housed within a refurbished colonial house, is flanked by an imposing glass display of bottles from its impressive wine collection. Lunch sees a good value set menu while at dinner the flexible menu allows for any combination of appetiser, pasta and main course. Signature dishes include squid ink tonnarelli, loin of lamb with a herb crust and chocolate mousse.

这意大利餐厅置身于殖民地建筑的一隅，穿过放满餐酒的走廊，先映入眼帘的是缤纷雅致的画作，二十四个座位分成两行分布在内，予人舒适之感。午膳可点选套餐；晚间可从餐单选取三至五道菜，自由组合头盘、意大利面条、主菜及甜点。酒单中能找到不少罕见的限量或旧年份佳酿，嗜杯中物者绝不能错过。

TEL. 6733 0209
29 Scotts Road
史各士路29号
www.buonaterra.com.sg

■ PRICE 价钱
Lunch 午膳
set 套餐 $ 48-68
Dinner 晚膳
set 套餐 $ 128-168

■ OPENING HOURS 营业时间
Lunch 午膳 12:00-14:30 (L.O.)
Dinner 晚膳 18:00-22:00 (L.O.)

■ ANNUAL AND WEEKLY CLOSING 休息日期
Closed Saturday and Public Holidays lunch; Sunday
周六及公众假期午膳；周日休息

CENTRAL 中区

TEL. 6222 3938
323 New Bridge Road
新桥路323号

■ **PRICE** 价钱
Lunch 午膳
à la carte 点菜 $ 30-70
Dinner 晚膳
à la carte 点菜 $ 30-70

■ **OPENING HOURS** 营业时间
Lunch 午膳 11:30-14:00 (L.O.)
Dinner 晚膳 17:30-22:00 (L.O.)

CENTRAL 中区

🍴🍽

CAPITAL
首都
Cantonese • Traditional
粤菜 • 传统

When you can claim to have been the first restaurant in Singapore to have served hairy crabs then it's little wonder you have plenty of customers and lots of regulars. The third generation of the Cheong family run the show these days, with Dad cooking, Mum serving and assorted relatives assisting. Classic Cantonese cooking is what they offer, but if it's the season go for the great value hairy crab menu – or just pop in and grab some to take home.

这家历史悠久的粤菜酒家，主要供应经典粤菜及烧味如鹅味烧鸭，已传至第三代。掌厨的是东主的父亲，其母则带领一众亲戚在店面服务客人。每到大闸蟹季节，这家号称狮城首家供应大闸蟹的酒家皆挤满了食客，为的是享用大闸蟹套餐。食客亦可将蟹买回家按自己喜欢的方式烹调。

CHAR
叉

Cantonese · Neighbourhood
粤菜 · 亲切

Cantonese roast meats prepared in a traditional way (with just a hint of Western style) lure plenty of customers to this relaxed and friendly restaurant. There's roast duck and crispy pork belly but it's the meltingly tender BBQ pork that really stands out; other Cantonese dishes on offer include seafood and stir-fried noodles. It occupies two floors – the ground floor's large round tables make it better suited to family gatherings.

设计简约随意并富现代感,地面层设有大圆桌适合家庭用餐,楼上一层有小酒吧和方桌,适合年轻人聚会。主打广式烧味,传统做法混合西式烹调法或调味料。一定要试叉烧,外观和味道都有浓浓的怀旧气息,色深带多肥脂,入口即溶却不油腻。餐厅还供应广式小菜、海鲜和粉面。

 ♿70

TEL. 6842 7759
363 Jalan Besar
惹兰勿刹363号
www.char.com.sg

■ **PRICE** 价钱
Lunch 午膳
à la carte 点菜 $ 20-40
Dinner 晚膳
à la carte 点菜 $ 20-40

■ **OPENING HOURS** 营业时间
Lunch 午膳 11:30-14:00 (L.O.)
Dinner 晚膳 18:00-21:30 (L.O.)

■ **ANNUAL AND WEEKLY CLOSING**
休息日期
Closed Monday 周一休息

CENTRAL 中区

CENTRAL 中区

TEL. 6224 4188

61 Tras Street
道拉实街61号
www.chefstable.sg

■ **PRICE** 价钱
Friday lunch 周五午膳
set 套餐 $ 55
Dinner 晚膳
set 套餐 $ 98-150

■ **OPENING HOURS** 营业时间
Friday lunch 周五午膳
12:00-14:00 (L.O.)
Dinner 晚膳 18:00-22:00 (L.O.)

■ **ANNUAL AND WEEKLY CLOSING**
休息日期
Closed Sunday and Monday
周日及周一休息

CHEF'S TABLE

European contemporary • Simple
时尚欧陆菜 • 简朴

What started as a cookery school was transformed into a restaurant in 2015 – it's in Tanjong Pagar but not the easiest place to spot. 28 ingredients, imported from around the world, are prepared each day and from them the chef will then improvise a dish of a largely European persuasion. What's more, they keep a record of your booking and what you ate to ensure that on your next visit you're offered something different.

餐厅原为主厨开班授徒的场地，于2015年转变成以厨师发力挂帅的食店。主厨每天会准备28款食材，食材来自世界各地。厨师每天随兴创作的菜式，结集了欧陆时尚风味，清淡却味美，意在显出食材的天然味道。特别的是，食客每次到来都能尝到新菜式，因服务员会记下你每次的到访，以免给你重复的菜式。

CHERRY GARDEN
櫻桃園

Cantonese • Exotic décor
粤菜•异国风情

Grace, style and opulence are the hallmarks of this revered Cantonese restaurant within the Mandarin Oriental. A wall of windows lets natural light flood the room at lunch, while at night the well-spaced tables ensure plenty of privacy for intimate dinners. The dishes, from velvety congee to delicious dumplings, are prepared with considerable care. A well-priced weekend dim sum menu offers a great way of experiencing the kitchen's ability.

粗糙的石砖墙、高悬着的红灯笼，中式古典木门后，是布置富丽堂皇、古意盎然的中菜馆。一道通往花园的玻璃门、一列偌大的玻璃窗，直接透射进内的自然光令房间充满生气。皮薄如透明、内馅汁丰味浓的意式西葫芦水晶饺滋味无穷，黑椒鳕鱼金网卷令人回味。周末和公众假期设有两组点心早午餐时段。

 ⛄ ⌖24 ◐

TEL. 6885 3500

Mandarin Oriental Hotel, Level 5, 5 Raffles Avenue, Marina Square

莱佛士道5号滨海广场
文华东方酒店5层

www.mandarinoriental.com/singapore

■ **PRICE** 价钱
Lunch 午膳
set 套餐 $ 52-138
à la carte 点菜 $ 45-420
Dinner 晚膳
set 套餐 $ 78-138
à la carte 点菜 $ 45-420

■ **OPENING HOURS** 营业时间
Lunch 午膳 12:00-14:30 (L.O.)
Dinner 晚膳 18:30-22:30 (L.O.)

CENTRAL 中区

◎🍴

TEL. 6258 4846

1 Goldhill Plaza, #01-19/21

金岭广场1号#01-19/21

www.daluca.com.sg

■ **PRICE** 价钱
Lunch 午膳
set 套餐 $ 27
à la carte 点菜 $ 45-120
Dinner 晚膳
set 套餐 $ 128
à la carte 点菜 $ 45-120

■ **OPENING HOURS** 营业时间
Lunch 午膳 12:00-14:30 (L.O.)
Dinner 晚膳 18:00-22:30 (L.O.)

■ **ANNUAL AND WEEKLY CLOSING**
休息日期
Closed Monday and Tuesday
周一及周二休息

🍴🍽

DA LUCA
Italian · Trattoria
意大利菜·意式酒馆

There's something about eating in an unpretentious family-run Italian restaurant that makes the world seem a better place. The eponymous Luca and his wife have created a friendly little spot two minutes' walk from Novena Station. He hails from Tuscany and his menu features the classics of Italian cuisine – the set lunch menu is terrific value, the daily specials are always worth trying and dishes are generously sized.

友善及家庭式意大利小酒馆风格的餐厅,餐牌主题为经典意大利菜,但并不包括薄饼在内。生于托斯卡纳的厨师主理的菜式味道正宗而地道。以优惠价钱提供的午市套餐,不光味美且分量充足,经济实惠。厨师最爱向客人推荐每日精选。餐酒单内含高中低价钱的意国佳酿任你挑选。

DB BISTRO & OYSTER BAR

French · Contemporary
法国菜 · 时尚

Daniel Boulud's bistros are synonymous with stylish surroundings, slick service and menus that offer classic French bistro dishes alongside American favourites. The 'Original Daniel Boulud burger' is always worth ordering but you should also explore those dishes which make great use of quality fish and shellfish from around the world. The restaurant comes with an appealingly authentic French bistro feel and there's an oyster bar at the front.

设计时尚的餐馆，掺杂了巴黎地下车通道的装潢风格，感觉随意舒适。此店的烹调和美食概念源自法国小酒馆的风格，朴实而不卖弄花巧，个别食品或带美国风味：海鲜柜台上的生蚝和贝壳类海产，还有美味的汉堡包，令人回味无穷！建议尝尝主厨原创、加了鹅肝的汉堡包。

☁ 🅿 ⟷22 ◔▯

TEL. 6688 8525

The Shoppes at Marina Bay Sands, Galleria Level, #B1-48, 10 Bayfront Avenue

贝弗兰道10号
滨海湾金沙购物商城#B1-48
www.dbbistro.com/singapore/

■ **PRICE** 价钱
Lunch 午膳
set 套餐 $ 32-52
à la carte 点菜 $ 55-140
Dinner 晚膳
set 套餐 $ 52-62
à la carte 点菜 $ 55-140

■ **OPENING HOURS** 营业时间
12:00-23:00 (L.O.)
Weekends 周末 11:00-22:00 (L.O.)

CENTRAL 中区

TEL. 6885 3500

**Mandarin Oriental Hotel, Level 5,
5 Raffles Avenue, Marina Square**

莱佛士道5号滨海广场
文华东方酒店5层

www.mandarinoriental.com/
singapore

CENTRAL 中区

■ **PRICE** 价钱
Lunch 午膳
set 套餐 $ 36-158
à la carte 点菜 $ 65-150
Dinner 晚膳
set 套餐 $ 88-148
à la carte 点菜 $ 65-150

■ **OPENING HOURS** 营业时间
Lunch 午膳 12:00-14:30 (L.O.)
Weekend lunch 周末午膳
12:00-15:00 (L.O.)
Dinner 晚膳 18:30-22:30 (L.O.)

DOLCE VITA

Italian • Mediterranean
意大利菜 • 地中海风

The poolside location adds to the appeal of this bright Italian restaurant – the perfect spot in which to enjoy the 'high life'. All regions of Italy are represented but there is a subtle southern slant; signature dishes include seafood soup and red prawn spaghetti – around 80% of the ingredients are flown in from Italy. The relaxing atmosphere and charming service make it a good choice for family gatherings; weekend brunch is also popular.

餐厅名称有高尚生活之意，随意的布置看起来却醒目活泼，令人心情愉悦。来自罗马的厨师对食材选择严谨，八成材料由意大利进口，菜单上沿用的是传统食谱，偏向南部风味的菜式带少许现代元素。招牌菜有托斯卡纳海鲜汤、红虾意大利面条和布拉塔奶酪帕马火腿。精选的餐酒单供应优质的意国小型酒庄佳酿。

EMPRESS
皇后

Cantonese · Contemporary
粤菜 · 时尚

The designers of this chic and contemporary Cantonese restaurant, courtesy of The Privé Group, have made the most of its great location within the Asian Civilisations Museum and facing the Singapore River. As such, it's one of those rare places that works just as well for a business lunch as it does for a gathering of friends or a romantic dinner. The menu is a mix of traditional and more modern dishes, with roast meats a speciality.

坐落于亚洲文明博物馆内,古建筑遗风搭配时尚雅致的装潢,典雅中别具韵味。敞开着的玻璃窗门,让阳光遍洒至每个角落,清新的空气弥漫一室,同时将室内和户外区串连起来,不论置身户外还是室内也能尽览新加坡河的壮丽景色。厨师选用世界各地的食材重新演绎的粤菜带点现代风味。附设的酒吧适合各种聚会。

🛇 🏠 ⟨ 🍴 P ⟷14 ◖◗ 🎨

TEL. 6776 0777

Asian Civilisations Museum #01-03, 1 Empress Place

皇后坊1号亚洲文明博物馆#01-03

www.empress.com.sg

■ **PRICE** 价钱
Lunch 午膳
set 套餐 $ 38-58
à la carte 点菜 $ 40-75
Dinner 晚膳
set 套餐 $ 88-108
à la carte 点菜 $ 40-75

■ **OPENING HOURS** 营业时间
Lunch 午膳 11:30-14:30 (L.O.)
Weekend lunch 周末午膳
11:00-15:30 (L.O.)
Dinner 晚膳 18:00-22:45 (L.O.)

CENTRAL 中区

CENTRAL 中区

P ⊕24 ⇔ ☺🍴

TEL. 6222 1616

16 Jiak Chuan Road

若泉路16号

www.esquina.com.sg

■ **PRICE 价钱**
Lunch 午膳
set 套餐 $ 28-38
à la carte 点菜 $ 30-80
Dinner 晚膳
set 套餐 $ 108
à la carte 点菜 $ 30-80

■ **OPENING HOURS 营业时间**
Lunch 午膳 12:00-14:30 (L.O.)
Dinner 晚膳 18:00-22:30 (L.O.)

■ **ANNUAL AND WEEKLY CLOSING**
休息日期
Closed Monday and Saturday lunch;
Sunday 周一、周六午膳及周日休息

🍴◯

ESQUINA

Spanish • Tapas bar
西班牙菜 • 西班牙小食吧

On an 'esquina' just off Keong Saik Road is an old shophouse that lends itself very nicely to this hip Spanish restaurant. Grab one of the tractor seat stools at the counter and watch the chefs in action. Their small plates are original and confidently prepared; the flavours are distinct and the imported ingredients are excellent. The great soundtrack adds to the vibe and there's a very good value menu offered at lunchtime.

充满西欧时尚风情的餐厅，以动听的音乐筑构出和谐舒适的气氛。坐在吧台前的吧椅上看着厨师烹调食物，感觉悠闲写意。主厨虽年轻，烹调及呈上小碟美食予食客时却是信心充足。带有个人风格、外形精致的西班牙菜式，选用优质食材，加上细腻的烹调技巧，味道很棒。中午套餐物有所值，值得一试。

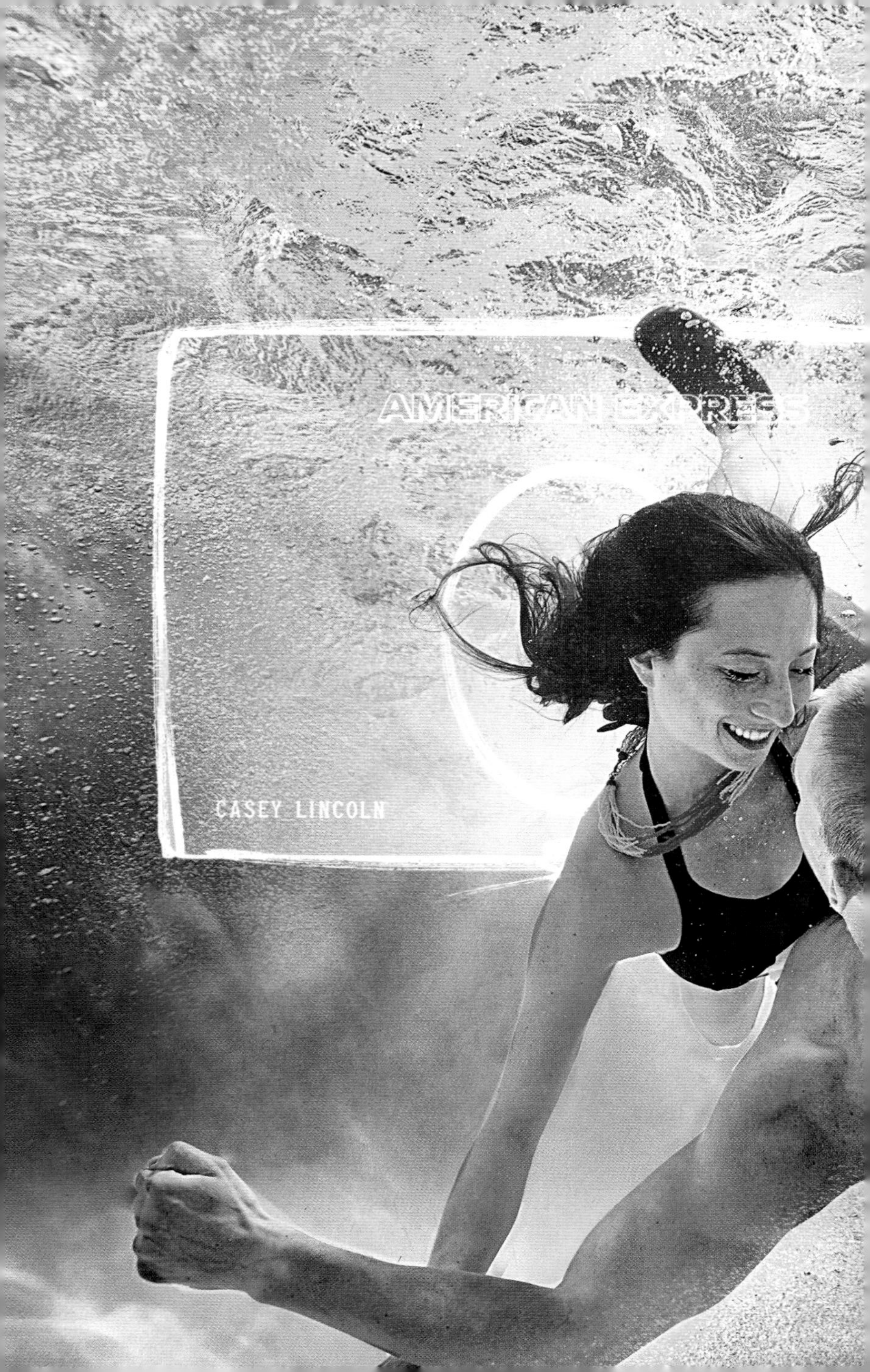
AMERICAN EXPRESS
CASEY LINCOLN

IT'S HIGH SPIRITS ON THE HIGH SEAS

Enjoy a holiday you'll never forget with your Platinum Card®.
Another extraordinary way American Express has got your back.

Call 6295 6293 or email us at PlatCard@aexp.com to express your interest.

FAT COW

Japanese steakhouse • Minimalist

日式扒房 • 简约

The ground floor of a medical centre is an unlikely place to find a Japanese steakhouse but it's worth seeking out. The restaurant specialises in various grades of Wagyu from five prefectures in Japan, along with breeds from Australia. The meat is charcoal-grilled but you can also opt for sukiyaki or shabu-shabu. To get the best from the experience, avoid the first dining room and sit at the counter to watch the chef in action behind the individual stove.

日本大厨和其团队就在餐柜台后为你预备食物。从处理刺身到如何裁切牛肉的各个部位，都能一览无遗。这儿的和牛来自至少五個日本縣市和澳洲的著名农场。食客选择和牛的级别后，厨师会以木炭烤煮，当然，你可以选择以寿喜烧或火锅形式烹调。日本清酒和威士忌酒单看来蛮吸引，何妨浅尝一杯？

P ♿ 24 🚻 ⓒ🍴

TEL. 6735 0308

**Camden Medical Centre,
#01-01/02, 1 Orchard Boulevard**

乌节林荫道1号
卡姆登医疗中心#01-01/02

www.fat-cow.com.sg

■ **PRICE** 价钱
Lunch 午膳
set 套餐 $ 30-120
à la carte 点菜 $ 80-280
Dinner 晚膳
set 套餐 $ 280
à la carte 点菜 $ 80-280

■ **OPENING HOURS** 营业时间
Lunch 午膳 12:00-14:30 (L.O.)
Dinner 晚膳 18:00-22:00 (L.O.)
Friday & Saturday dinner
周五及周六晚膳 18:00-22:30 (L.O.)

■ **ANNUAL AND WEEKLY CLOSING**
休息日期
Closed Lunar New Year and first day of New Year
农历新年及元旦休息

CENTRAL 中区

♿ ⎙12 🚗 ☏🍴 ♨

TEL. 6222 6861
#01-01, 64 Tras Street
道拉实街64号#01-01
www.fleurdesel.com.sg

■ **PRICE** 价钱
Lunch 午膳
set 套餐 $ 48-58
à la carte 点菜 $ 75-180
Dinner 晚膳
set 套餐 $ 108-168
à la carte 点菜 $ 75-180

■ **OPENING HOURS** 营业时间
Lunch 午膳 12:00-14:00 (L.O.)
Dinner 晚膳 18:30-22:00 (L.O.)

■ **ANNUAL AND WEEKLY CLOSING**
休息日期
Closed Saturday lunch and Sunday
周六午膳及周日休息

🍴⭘

FLEUR DE SEL
French • Classic
法国菜•经典

You'll find the artisanal French salt from which the restaurant gets its name on each table – but you won't need it because the owner-chef has worked for some of the world's greatest chefs and knows what he's doing. At this 'bistro de luxe' he delivers classical French cuisine prepared in a modern, lighter style – and that makes it easy to save room for his signature Baba. There's a good choice of clarets and burgundies to accompany the dishes.

盐之花是法国顶级海盐,店主以此为餐厅命名,有何特别寓意?高级法国小馆格调的餐馆,由富经验的主厨兼店主Alexandre亲自领导,提供以现代方法烹调、外形带点时尚的经典法国美食。以高级食材组成的餐单和一系列波尔多、勃艮第美酒,足证餐馆走的确是高格调之风。甜点La Baba是主厨的招牌美食。

FOC

Spanish · Fashionable

西班牙菜 · 时髦

'Fine fun food from Barcelona' is how the eponymous chef describes his Singaporean outpost. He's brought along the flavours of Catalonia which he blends with modern cooking techniques to create original and exciting dishes. The surroundings are relaxed and always furiously busy, with the principal players in the operation represented by huge papier mâché heads. Ask for a seat at the counter to get the most out of the experience.

打着精致有趣的巴塞罗那美食的旗号，此餐馆是西班牙厨师Nandu Jubany在这儿的据点。时尚、繁忙、朝气勃勃，是不拘泥的格调。小碟西班牙菜式，在传统的基础上注入了新元素，味道与口感的融合创造出独特的原创风味，让味觉得到不一样的体验。酒吧台顶以店主和主厨的大型黏土头像作装饰，煞是有趣。

🛋 ⇔8 ⇔ ⓘ🍴

TEL. 6100 4040

40 Hong Kong Street

香港街40号

www.focrestaurant.com

■ **PRICE** 价钱
Lunch 午膳
à la carte 点菜 $ 45-205
Dinner 晚膳
à la carte 点菜 $ 45-205

■ **OPENING HOURS** 营业时间
Lunch 午膳 12:00-13:45 (L.O.)
Dinner 晚膳 18:00-21:45 (L.O.)
Friday & Saturday dinner
周五及周六晚膳 18:00-22:15 (L.O.)

■ **ANNUAL AND WEEKLY CLOSING**
休息日期
Closed Sunday lunch 周日午膳休息

CENTRAL 中区

CENTRAL 中区

 ⚭22

TEL. 6690 7564

**One Fullerton, #02-06,
1 Fullerton Road**
浮尔顿路1号浮尔顿一号#02-06
www.forlino.com

■ **PRICE 价钱**
Lunch 午膳
set 套餐 $ 38-88
à la carte 点菜 $ 80-150
Dinner 晚膳
set 套餐 $ 118-148
à la carte 点菜 $ 80-150

■ **OPENING HOURS 营业时间**
Lunch 午膳 12:00-14:30 (L.O.)
Dinner 晚膳 18:30-22:30 (L.O.)

FORLINO

Italian • Elegant
意大利菜•典雅

Italian flair, Japanese precision and super-fresh ingredients combine to create delicious dishes in this plush dining room with great views. At lunch most are in for the quick business menu but if you opt for the à la carte you get to see what the kitchen can really do, with dishes like linguine with Hokkaido sea urchin and bottarga, or slow-cooked black cod with tripe and white polenta. For dessert, few see past the signature tiramisu.

混入了日本风味以传统手法和新鲜食材制作的意大利菜风味正宗、味道可口。周一至周五午市时段会提供三道菜的商务午餐，当然，有空档慢慢品尝美食的，可以选择单点菜单上的菜式。面质幼滑的香蒜海胆意大利面条(Linguine Pasta 'Aglioe Olio' ai Ricci di Mare)和厨师推介的甜品提拉米苏是不错的选择。

GAIG

Spanish · Friendly
西班牙菜 · 友善

This relaxed and friendly restaurant is run by the same family as its namesake in Barcelona. It serves Catalan dishes prepared the same way as they were back in the 19th Century, such as cannelloni and quail Alcántara-style. The chef shops for the best produce in local markets three times a week. The wine menu has a great Spanish selection at very reasonable prices. Make sure you finish up with their unmissable Catalan crème brûlée.

自巴塞罗那的总店起至今历经五代，承传的除了是传统菜式，还有厨师始终如一地推广地道加泰罗尼亚菜的热诚。每周三次亲自到市场挑选新鲜时令食材，为的是运用优质在地食材将意大利面卷等逾百年传统菜式的精粹呈现出来。餐厅环境温馨自在，让客人可以放松地饱尝一顿西班牙佳肴和美酒，以加泰罗尼焦糖炖蛋作结，更是乐事。

TEL. 6221 2134
16 Stanley Street
史坦利街16号
www.restaurantgaig.com

■ **PRICE** 价钱
Lunch 午膳
set 套餐 $ 38-45
à la carte 点菜 $ 40-60
Dinner 晚膳
à la carte 点菜 $ 80-120

■ **OPENING HOURS** 营业时间
Lunch 午膳 12:00-14:00 (L.O.)
Dinner 晚膳 18:00-21:45 (L.O.)

■ **ANNUAL AND WEEKLY CLOSING**
休息日期
Closed Saturday lunch and Sunday
周六午膳及周日休息

CENTRAL 中区

20

TEL. 6338 5498

36 Tras Street

道拉实街36号

www.gattopardo.com.sg

■ PRICE 价钱

Lunch 午膳
set 套餐 $ 32-60
à la carte 点菜 $ 60-120
Dinner 晚膳
set 套餐 $ 80-118
à la carte 点菜 $ 60-120

■ OPENING HOURS 营业时间

Lunch 午膳 12:00-14:30 (L.O.)
Dinner 晚膳 18:30-22:00 (L.O.)

■ ANNUAL AND WEEKLY CLOSING 休息日期

Closed December 25-26; Saturday lunch and Sunday
12月25-26日、周六午膳及周日休息

GATTOPARDO N

Sicilian • Mediterranean

西西里菜•地中海风

The restored shophouse complements nicely the old world charm of the dining room. The Sicilian chef is keen to let people know all about Sicily and seafood is his speciality. Half of the menu changes quarterly while signature dishes such as seafood stew in a terracotta pot and red shrimp black truffle ravioli stay on; the lunch set menu rotates weekly. Diners also come for the salt-baked fish with tableside service, and the homemade pasta.

厨师抱着将家乡菜发扬光大的心思，将善用茴香、番红花等缤纷香料的西西里菜式呈现於客人眼前。菜单主打海鲜类，设计上特别有一半的菜式是随时令更换，以将本地坐享各种优质食材的优势尽量发挥；而午膳套餐更每周更新一次。招牌菜是海鲜锅(Zuppa)及意大利饺(Ravioli)，也有人为餐厅自制的意大利面及席前準备的盐焗鱼(Pesce Al Sale)慕名而来。

GINZA ROKUKAKUTEI
銀座六覺燈

Kushiage • Intimate
串炸·亲密

The first outpost outside Japan of its famed namesake in Osaka adheres to the same standard of meticulous care and food quality as its flagship, but with one difference – the skewers here are fried in rice bran oil instead of beef tallow or lard. The ingredients are imported from Hokkaido and the skewers are spun to remove any excess oil. Where it differs is that wine pairing is available.

为了向外推广大阪文化，店主选址新加坡开设分店，希望透过顶级的串炸配以异国佳酿房获食客的心。有别于日本店，此处采用米糠油炸制食材，好处是油温高时不损料理品质，且会散发出独特香气；厨师亦更容易去掉食物上多余的油份。为了确保客人品尝到更地道的日本风味，厨房中的炉具更是与日本店的一式一样，而食材亦是每周两次从北海道空运到店。

⊖12 ⇌ ◐ 🍴 🕸
TEL. 6266 1077
Odeon Towers, #01-04,
331 North Bridge Road

桥北路331号
奥迪安大厦#01-04

■ **PRICE** 价钱
Lunch 午膳
set 套餐 $ 20-58
Dinner 晚膳
set 套餐 $ 98-134

■ **OPENING HOURS** 营业时间
Lunch 午膳 12:00-14:00 (L.O.)
Dinner 晚膳 17:00-22:30 (L.O.)

■ **ANNUAL AND WEEKLY CLOSING**
休息日期
Closed Sunday and Public Holidays
周日及公众假期休息

CENTRAL 中区

&. 🖐 🅿 ⇔10 ⓞ🍴

TEL. 6432 7482

Conrad Centennial Hotel, Level 3, 2 Temasek Boulevard

淡马锡林荫道2号
康莱德酒店3层

www.conradsingapore.com

■ **PRICE** 价钱
Lunch 午膳
set 套餐 $ 48-118
à la carte 点菜 $ 40-150
Dinner 晚膳
set 套餐 $ 68-118
à la carte 点菜 $ 40-150

■ **OPENING HOURS** 营业时间
Lunch 午膳 11:30-14:15 (L.O.)
Sunday lunch
周日午膳 10:30-14:15 (L.O.)
Dinner 晚膳 18:30-22:00 (L.O.)

🍴ⓞ

GOLDEN PEONY
金牡丹

Cantonese · Elegant
粤菜 · 典雅

There's a sophisticated and elegant feel to this spacious and comfortable Chinese restaurant on the 3rd floor of the Conrad Centennial hotel. Like the decoration, the Cantonese cuisine adds contemporary touches to a classic base. The best known signature dishes of the longstanding chef include double-boiled baby abalone soup with conpoy and bamboo, and braised Dong Po pork belly with crispy bun. Dim sum is also popular here.

位于康莱德酒店店内，时尚与古典融合为一的布置、宽敞且高雅的环境，与由经验厨师预备的粤菜配合得天衣无缝。鲜螺头炖竹笙柱脯鲍鱼仔汤及东坡肉伴炸馒头是招牌菜。点心种类不少且素质不错。

GORDON GRILL

European contemporary · Cosy
时尚欧陆菜·舒适

Those with fond memories of European-style grill rooms will like Gordon Grill. A feature of Goodwood Park hotel for over 50 years, the restaurant is famed for its meat trolley service which is wheeled over to each table. Along with the meat and plentiful supplies of seafood from the grill, you can expect French-inspired classic dishes. It's a good choice for a quiet business lunch, a romantic dinner or weekend family outings.

餐厅自1963年开业以来一直供应各式欧陆风味美食，如烤法式田螺、龙虾汤、牛面颊肉伴红酒汁、苹果馅饼等。特别的是手推车会被推到餐厅每个角落，让食客目睹切割、量重等过程。适合商务午餐、烛光晚餐及周末家庭聚会。毗邻的酒吧是进餐前后把酒谈心的好地方。

TEL. 6730 1744
Goodwood Park Hotel,
22 Scotts Road
史各士路22号良木园酒店
www.goodwoodparkhotel.com

■ **PRICE 价钱**
Lunch 午膳
set 套餐 $ 55-68
à la carte 点菜 $ 80-160
Dinner 晚膳
set 套餐 $ 68-128
à la carte 点菜 $ 80-160

■ **OPENING HOURS 营业时间**
Lunch 午膳 12:00-14:30 (L.O.)
Dinner 晚膳 19:00-22:00 (L.O.)

CENTRAL 中区

🍴🅿 ⇔38 ☐🍴 ⚒

TEL. 6338 8955

#01-03, 36 Purvis Street
巴米士街36号#01-03
www.gunthers.com.sg

■ **PRICE 价钱**
Lunch 午膳
set 套餐 $ 38-350
à la carte 点菜 $ 70-220
Dinner 晚膳
set 套餐 $ 148-350
à la carte 点菜 $ 70-220

■ **OPENING HOURS 营业时间**
Lunch 午膳 12:00-14:30 (L.O.)
Dinner 晚膳 18:30-22:00 (L.O.)

■ **ANNUAL AND WEEKLY CLOSING**
休息日期
Closed Saturday lunch and Sunday
周六午膳及周日休息

🍴🍴

GUNTHER'S

French • Intimate
法国菜•亲密

The owner-chef worked in some well-known restaurants in his native Belgium before coming to Singapore. He may describe his cooking as "simple, honest and down-to-earth" but typical dishes include angel hair pasta with Oscietra caviar, roast rack of black pig, and fine apple tart. Many regulars wait until they've seen the tray of the day's special ingredients before ordering, however.

不显眼的外观，一不小心便会错过这家瑟缩于小街一角的餐馆！厨师烹调的宗旨一如店子的外观：简单、平实。黑椒帕尔马干酪烤洋葱、鱼子酱凉拌天使面、兰姆酒葡萄冰淇淋等都能在这儿吃到。食客多在观看每日精选食材后才点菜。重新装修过的餐室以富现代感的线条作点缀，令餐室更添格调。

CENTRAL 中区

HASHIDA

Sushi • Modern

寿司 • 现代

2016 saw this sushi restaurant move to bigger premises and it now has three separate rooms, each with their own counter. There are three menu options for lunch while at dinner only an omakase is offered. For the sushi, fish comes four times a week from Tokyo's Tsukiji Market and twice a week from Hokkaido, with selected white-hulled rice also imported from Japan. The signature dish is monkfish liver with sea eel sauce.

搬迁后的餐厅，仍然走简约与禅味并重的和风路线，空间较前宽敞，共有三个餐室；每个餐室均有独立寿司吧台。午膳有三组餐单供食客选择，而晚膳只提供厨师发办餐单。鱼生每周六次从东京筑地市场或北海道空运到店，寿司米用的也是日本进口白米。鳗鱼汁安康鱼肝是招牌菜。

P ⊕16 ⇄ ◖❙❙
TEL. 6733 2114
Mandarin Gallery, #04-16,
333A Orchard Road
乌节路333A号文华购物廊#04-16
www.hashida.com.sg

■ **PRICE 价钱**
Lunch 午膳
set 套餐 $ 80-250
Dinner 晚膳
set 套餐 $ 280-500

■ **OPENING HOURS** 营业时间
Lunch 午膳 12:00-14:00 (L.O.)
Tuesday lunch 周二午膳
12:30-14:00 (L.O.)
Dinner 晚膳 19:00-21:00 (L.O.)

■ **ANNUAL AND WEEKLY CLOSING**
休息日期
Closed Monday 周一休息

CENTRAL 中区

🆂 ♿ 🍴

TEL. 6297 4294

11-17 Jalan Pisang
惹兰比山11-17号

■ **PRICE** 价钱
à la carte 点菜 $ 10-15

■ **OPENING HOURS** 营业时间
07:00-20:00 (L.O.)

■ **ANNUAL AND WEEKLY CLOSING**
休息日期
Closed Sunday 周日休息

🍴○

HJH MAIMUNAH (JALAN PISANG)

Malaysian · Simple
马来西亚菜 · 简朴

In a narrow street behind Masjid Sultan mosque is a simple Malaysian restaurant that's always busy – and it's easy to see why: the ingredients are fresh, the food is delicious and the prices are affordable. Around 70% of dishes are Malaysian and 30% Indonesian; it's mostly self-service and the dishes to go for include Sundanese grilled chicken, beef rendang, lemak siput and tahu telur. The upstairs room is slightly more comfortable.

餐厅位于苏丹回教堂背后狭长街道上，色彩斑斓的食材放满柜台，煞是吸引，叫食客去而复返的是那用料新鲜、风味正宗、味道浓郁可口的各式佳肴，当中七成属于马来西亚菜式、三成是印尼美食。圣丹斯烤鸡、椰浆蜗牛、烤鱼、冷当牛肉等都不错，且价钱相宜。食客需自行在食物柜台前选购食物。

HUA TING
華廳

Cantonese · Elegant
粤菜 · 典雅

The cooking at Orchard Hotel's Cantonese restaurant comes with a contemporary flourish, with signature dishes like sautéed prawns with avocado and salted egg yolk; stewed oxtail with garlic in brown sauce; and crispy roast duck. If you've come for dim sum do try the steamed bean curd with assorted vegetables. The room is comfortable and classically decorated and is run with considerable professionalism by a team willing to offer advice.

要进入这家位处酒店内的高级粤菜厅，千万别穿短裤或拖鞋，餐厅经理会把衣冠不整的人拒诸门外。餐厅装潢典雅，职员态度友善，来自香港的主厨锺师傅为广东菜添上不少创意，这里的点心尤其出色，特别推荐双色两味鸳鸯虾球、蒜子红焖牛尾、脆皮烧鸭及点心腐皮上素包。

🅿 ♻30 Ⓒ🍴

TEL. 6739 6666

Orchard Hotel, Level 2, 442 Orchard Road
乌节路442号乌节大酒店2层
www.huatingsingapore.sg

■ **PRICE 价钱**
Lunch 午膳
set 套餐 $ 48-88
à la carte 点菜 $ 50-200
Dinner 晚膳
set 套餐 $ 98-168
à la carte 点菜 $ 50-200

■ **OPENING HOURS 营业时间**
Lunch 午膳 11:30-14:30 (L.O.)
Weekends & eve of Public Holidays lunch 周末及公众假期前夕午膳 11:00-14:30 (L.O.)
Dinner 晚膳 18:00-22:00 (L.O.)

CENTRAL 中区

♿ 🅿 🍽60 ⚭🍴

TEL. 6732 2232

**Great World City, #02-05A/6,
1 Kim Seng Promenade**
金声河畔道1号世界城#02-05A/6

www.imperialtreasure.com

■ **PRICE 价钱**
Lunch 午膳
à la carte 点菜 $ 40-100
Dinner 晚膳
à la carte 点菜 $ 40-100

■ **OPENING HOURS 营业时间**
Lunch 午膳 11:30-14:30 (L.O.)
Saturday lunch 周六午膳
11:00-14:45 (L.O.)
Sunday lunch 周日午膳
10:30-14:45 (L.O.)
Dinner 晚膳 18:00-22:30 (L.O.)

🍴○

IMPERIAL TREASURE CANTONESE CUISINE (GREAT WORLD CITY)
御寶軒 (世界城)

Cantonese • Classic
粤菜•经典

The fish tanks and wine cellar at the entrance set the tone for this well-dressed Cantonese restaurant, with its wood panelling and splashes of red. It offers a comprehensive selection of Cantonese dishes, with set menus for 2 to 10 people. Look out for the braised fish maw with goose web. Dim sum, prepared by the restaurant's Hong Kong chefs, is available daily. It is part of the Imperial Treasure Group, which has over 20 restaurants.

隶属御宝饮食集团旗下，经过入口的水族箱和酒柜，迎面的是以红色为主调的用餐区，红色吊灯、深木色陈设为餐厅添上了中国韵味。这儿提供各式受欢迎的广东菜肴，从经典的咕噜肉至令人垂涎的花胶焖鹅掌，包罗万有，更少不了由香港厨师主理的广式点心。亦设二至十人套餐。

IMPERIAL TREASURE SHANGHAI CUISINE
御園

Shanghainese • Contemporary
沪菜 • 时尚

Specialities at this Shanghainese restaurant, located among the various boutiques on the 4th floor of Ngee Ann City, include marinated jellyfish, Zhenjiang-style pork terrine, drunken chicken, sautéed shrimps, and stewed pork in brown sauce with steamed bun. The restaurant is also unusual in that it serves dim sum at dinner as well as lunch. When making your reservation, ask for one of the intimate cocoon-like booths.

不论在普通座位或隐秘的厢座,都能轻松、惬意地享用店内的上海菜肴。最受欢迎的菜式有海蜇头、镇江肴肉、醉鸡、油爆虾及红烧肉。有别于本地大部分中式餐厅,这里晚膳时段也供应点心。若对上海菜感到陌生,专业的服务员会助你一把。

&. P ⇔16 ©‖

TEL. 6836 6909
Ngee Ann City, #04-22,
391A Orchard Road
乌节路391A号义安城#04-22
www.imperialtreasure.com

■ **PRICE** 价钱
Lunch 午膳
set 套餐 $ 50-68
à la carte 点菜 $ 40-200
Dinner 晚膳
set 套餐 $ 50-68
à la carte 点菜 $ 40-200

■ **OPENING HOURS** 营业时间
Lunch 午膳 11:30-15:00 (L.O.)
Dinner 晚膳 18:00-22:15 (L.O.)

CENTRAL 中区

CENTRAL 中区

 ♿ 🅿 ⇧50 🍴

TEL. 6732 7838

**Paragon Shopping Centre,
#05-42/45, 290 Orchard Road**

乌节路290号百利宫#05-42/45

www.imperialtreasure.com

■ **PRICE 价钱**
Lunch 午膳
set 套餐 $ 78-98
à la carte 点菜 $ 50-200
Dinner 晚膳
set 套餐 $ 78-98
à la carte 点菜 $ 50-200

■ **OPENING HOURS 营业时间**
Lunch 午膳 11:30-15:00 (L.O.)
Dinner 晚膳 18:00-22:00 (L.O.)

🍴○

IMPERIAL TREASURE SUPER PEKING DUCK (PARAGON)
御寶至尊烤鴨店（百利宮）

Cantonese • Contemporary
粤菜 • 时尚

Considered the jewel in the crown of the Imperial Treasure group, this restaurant specialises in Peking duck and is divided into three rooms, with the main one largely kept for bigger parties. After roasting, the whole duck is sliced at the table with a fair degree of ceremony; the skin is crisp and the meat succulent. Don't ignore other dishes like poached Soou Hock fish fillet with chicken broth, and crispy rice roll for lunchtime dim sum. Booking is a must.

所属集团旗下餐厅中的珍宝，享负盛名的京式烤鸭选用马来西亚鸭种，厨師會即席将完整的鸭片成薄片，隆重得像宗教仪式！烤鸭皮薄香脆、肉质鲜美，难怪成为镇店菜式！烤鸭以外，浓鸡汤浸津白笋殼球亦同样用心制作，所使用鸡汤以老鸡熬制八小时而成，且每日鲜制两次。繁忙时间建议订座。六人或以上可点选套餐。

INDOCAFE - THE WHITE HOUSE

Peranakan · Traditional

娘惹菜 · 传统

Dark wood furniture and antiques add to the elegant colonial feel of this restaurant which lodges within a bungalow and also goes by the name of the 'The White House'. The menu is dominated by Penang-style Peranakan cuisine and, while the dishes look quite simple, their preparation involves the subtle blending of many spices and ingredients. The signature dishes include Rendang, Assam Laksa, and Kueh Pie Tee (pastry with turnips, prawns and crab).

黑、白色殖民风的平房，木地板、深色木家具、藤椅和众多的土生华人古董形成强烈风格。餐厅供应的菜肴结合了马来和华菜风味，卖相简朴，每一口都交织着多种调料、香料的复杂味道，扑鼻香气深藏层次，小金杯(Kueh Pie Tee)、巴东牛肉(Rendang Sapi)和阿参叻沙(Assam Laksa)都值得一试。

P ⇆8 ◖❙

TEL. 6733 2656

35 Scotts Road

史各士路35号

www.thehouseofindocafe.com

■ **PRICE** 价钱
Lunch 午膳
set 套餐 $ 39-59
à la carte 点菜 $ 45-60
Dinner 晚膳
set 套餐 $ 59
à la carte 点菜 $ 45-60

■ **OPENING HOURS** 营业时间
Lunch 午膳 12:00-14:00 (L.O.)
Dinner 晚膳 18:00-21:30 (L.O.)

CENTRAL 中区

  28

TEL. 6733 8388

**The Fullerton Hotel,
1 Fullerton Square**

浮尔顿广场1号富丽敦酒店

www.fullertonhotel.com

■ **PRICE 价钱**
Lunch 午膳
set 套餐 $ 48-98
à la carte 点菜 $ 50-100
Dinner 晚膳
set 套餐 $ 88-98
à la carte 点菜 $ 50-100

■ **OPENING HOURS 营业时间**
Lunch 午膳 11:30-14:30 (L.O.)
Dinner 晚膳 18:30-22:30 (L.O.)

JADE
玉楼

Chinese · Elegant
中国菜 · 典雅

Resplendent in silks, enriched by lacquered woods and engulfed by natural light, this elegant and sophisticated Chinese restaurant is just the sort of place you'd expect to find in the historic Fullerton hotel. Tables allow for much privacy by being large and well spaced and this adds to the restaurant's popularity with those who have entertaining to do. The menu blends the classics with the more modern and the care taken by the kitchen is obvious.

高高的天花、米白色调带有扭纹雕花边的墙身、白纱加丝绒窗帘、铺上白餐桌布的圆桌和设计时尚的中式靠背餐椅，展现出现代与传统融合为一的时尚典雅之美。看似不经意放在墙角的小株绿树，为餐馆平添一分自然之味。高水准的食物令人流连忘返！不论你无肉不欢或清心茹素，清炖冬瓜竹笙汤都能满足你。

JADE PALACE
金湖

Seafood • Traditional
海鲜 • 传统

Booking is advisable at this basement Cantonese seafood restaurant as it's a favourite of many. In terms of decoration and menu content, it has a pronounced Hong Kong feel, with the vast fish tank by the entrance providing plenty of menu items. Along with 12 claypot dishes, look out for steamed garoupa with ham and black mushrooms, and sautéed scallops. The impressive wine list is particularly strong in Bordeaux and Burgundy.

港式海鲜酒家，厨师和经理来自香港，装潢和餐单内容带着浓浓香港味。入口处鱼缸内新鲜的鱼、虾和蟹是最热点的食物，餐单包罗一系列传统广东小菜，冬菇火腿蒸斑片和橄榄炒带子鲜鱿为招牌菜。午市当然少不了广东点心。精选酒单由酷爱美酒的店东亲自挑选，罗列多款波尔多和勃艮地佳酿。

⇔60 ◐⟨

TEL. 6732 6628

Forum The Shopping Mall, #B1-13, 583 Orchard Road
乌节路583号福临购物中心#B1-13

■ **PRICE** 价钱
Lunch 午膳
set 套餐 $ 38-48
à la carte 点菜 $ 45-160
Dinner 晚膳
set 套餐 $ 78
à la carte 点菜 $ 45-160

■ **OPENING HOURS** 营业时间
Lunch 午膳 12:00-14:00 (L.O.)
Dinner 晚膳 18:00-22:00 (L.O.)

■ **ANNUAL AND WEEKLY CLOSING**
休息日期
Closed 2 days Lunar New Year
农历新年休息2天

CENTRAL 中区

TEL. 6732 0192
Cuppage Plaza, #04-02,
5 Koek Road
谷路5号卡佩芝广场#04-02
www.kapposhunsui.sg

■ **PRICE** 价钱
Dinner 晚膳
set 套餐 $ 150-300

■ **OPENING HOURS** 营业时间
Dinner 晚膳 18:00-21:00 (L.O.)

■ **ANNUAL AND WEEKLY CLOSING**
休息日期
Closed Monday 周一休息

CENTRAL 中区

KAPPO SHUNSUI Ⓝ
割烹旬水

Japanese • Simple
日本菜 • 简朴

It's not just about reserving a table if you want to sample its authentic omakase menu and its wonderful selection of over 80 different sakes, you also need to find this restaurant – its secretive entrance has no sign, just a frosted glass door and a bell. The chef is serious about every detail – even the dashi is made daily with kombu from Shiretoko and mineral water. A luxury menu is available upon pre-order five days ahead.

大隐隐于市，店外无招牌、不铺张，为的是让客人不受骚扰地品尝传统日式料理的真味。大厨对细节一丝不苟，高汤以矿泉水及来自知床的昆布每日鲜制，配以时令食材制作的厨师发办套餐令人惊艳。厨师会确保客人每次光临皆尝到不同菜式，更有逾八十款清酒供搭配。欲品尝三百元以上的套餐须提前五天预订。

KENG ENG KEE
瓊榮記

Singaporean • Simple
新加坡菜 • 简朴

This popular Cze Char restaurant may not be the most conveniently placed but it does some great dishes, like stir-fried ginger onion crab, coffee pork ribs and claypot duck with sea cucumber. The setting and environment are not unlike a hawker centre, although there is a smaller inside area that's air-conditioned. It provides mostly Hainanese cuisine, along with some Cantonese dishes – the stir-fries are particularly delicious.

这主营煮炒菜式的餐厅靠近工业区,就在亚历山大村美食中心后面,虽然地点不算方便,但其姜葱炒蟹、咖啡骨和海参鸡仍吸引不少本地人专程前往品尝。餐单尚包括广东菜,如镬气小炒、煲仔菜和炒粉面等。餐厅环境简单随意,设有半露天位置和面积较小的空调餐室,订座时可申明座位偏好。

TEL. 6272 1038
Blk 124, #01-136,
Bukit Merah Lane 1
红山1巷124座#01-136
www.kek.com.sg

■ **PRICE** 价钱
Lunch 午膳
à la carte 点菜 $ 15-30
Dinner 晚膳
à la carte 点菜 $ 15-30

■ **OPENING HOURS** 营业时间
Lunch 午膳 12:00-14:30 (L.O.)
Dinner 晚膳 17:00-22:00 (L.O.)

CENTRAL 中区

TEL. 6225 6897

85 Club Street

客纳街85号

www.langelus.sg

■ **PRICE** 价钱
Lunch 午膳
set 套餐 $ 38
à la carte 点菜 $ 65-125
Dinner 晚膳
set 套餐 $ 68
à la carte 点菜 $ 65-125

■ **OPENING HOURS** 营业时间
Lunch 午膳 12:00-14:00 (L.O.)
Dinner 晚膳 19:00-22:30 (L.O.)

■ **ANNUAL AND WEEKLY CLOSING**
休息日期
Closed Saturday lunch and Sunday
周六午膳及周日休息

L'ANGELUS

French • Bistro

法国菜 • 法式小餐馆

Chinatown may not be the most obvious part of town when you're looking for classic French food but that's where this bistro has been successfully pulling in customers since 1998. The great strength here is the passion of the two French owners and it is this that ensures that standards remain high. Signature dishes include homemade pâté and the ever-popular entrecôte – you'll be surprised at the size of the cut considering the price.

充满法国情调的店子，位于狮城著名的牛车水内，于1998年开业，东主为两名法国人，二人对于家乡菜的热情与热爱多年来不曾减退，店内供应的是经典和传统法国菜。招牌菜包括自家制鸡肝及猪肉酱、兰姆酒Blackmores和牛扒。令人惊喜的是，牛扒的分量足够让你大快朵颐。

LEWIN TERRACE

Innovative · Elegant

创新菜 · 典雅

In an appealingly leafy spot in Fort Canning Park you'll find this attractive colonial-style bungalow, built in 1908 for the eponymous Mr Lewin, the then chief of the Central Fire Station. Its cool white interior is a good spot for lunch, while the pleasant veranda is a better choice at night. The menus offer Japanese ingredients and precision, blended with both classic and modern French cuisine. This results in colourful dishes with delicate flavours.

位于绿树成荫的福康宁公园内，建于1908年，此小平房充满殖民时代气息。由富有经验的日籍大厨设计与烹调，选用日本食材，结合细腻的法国烹调技术和日本创意元素制作的小菜，虽有个别不太常见的食材搭配，但色彩鲜艳、味道独特可口。午市的梅套餐和晚市的赏味套餐最能让你体验法日相融的独特风味。

🏠 ≼ 🍴 🅿 ⇪40 ◐🍴

TEL. 6333 9905

**21 Lewin Terrace,
Fort Canning Park**

福康宁公园Lewin Terrace 21号

www.lewinterrace.com.sg

■ **PRICE 价钱**
Lunch 午膳
set 套餐 $ 48-128
à la carte 点菜 $ 65-170
Dinner 晚膳
set 套餐 $ 128-188
à la carte 点菜 $ 65-170

■ **OPENING HOURS 营业时间**
Lunch 午膳 12:00-14:00 (L.O.)
Dinner 晚膳 18:30-21:30 (L.O.)

CENTRAL 中区

CENTRAL 中区

 P ⟷22 ⛶ ⚏

TEL. 6688 7299

The Shoppes at Marina Bay Sands, Level 2 Dining, #02-02, 10 Bayfront Avenue

贝弗兰道10号
滨海湾金沙购物商城2层#02-02

www.longchim.com.sg

■ **PRICE 价钱**
Lunch 午膳
set 套餐 $ 25-69
à la carte 点菜 $ 50-90
Dinner 晚膳
set 套餐 $ 69
à la carte 点菜 $ 50-90

■ **OPENING HOURS 营业时间**
Lunch 午膳 11:30-14:30 (L.O.)
Dinner 晚膳 17:30-22:30 (L.O.)
Friday to Sunday 周五至周日
12:00-22:30 (L.O.)

🍴

LONG CHIM

Thai • Exotic décor
泰国菜•异国风情

Unlike at David Thompson's Nahm restaurant in Bangkok where he celebrates royal Thai cuisine, here at his Singapore outpost the focus is on 'street food'. It's a fun, vibrant spot, with friendly service and a busy open kitchen adding to the atmosphere. Dishes to look out for include Chiang Mai larp of chicken, crunchy pork on rice and the curries, which include sour orange curry of snakehead fish. Portions are generous and made for sharing.

木天花、木地板、木椅及餐桌，昏黄的灯光，回廊上的艺术涂鸦及开放式厨房，装潢时尚且富情调，气氛欢闹活泼，令人心情也随之愉快起来！以供应正宗泰国面食和小吃为主。青咖喱鸡的鸡块鲜嫩多汁、油分充足，十分美味。清迈兔治鸡肉及大虾炒泰式金边粉也是招牌菜之一。菜式分量蛮多，适宜与亲友共享。

...

LUKE'S (GEMMILL LANE)

Steakhouse · Classic
扒房 · 经典

There may be a branch in Orchard Road but this is their true home. Kick off with a cocktail at the attractive marble-topped bar before getting comfortable in the clubby, classically decorated restaurant with its leather seats and wood panelling. Crisp linen on the table and efficient staff complete the picture. The oysters, lobster and steaks are imported from the USA – with such good ingredients and accurate cooking it's hard to fault the end result.

大理石面酒吧台、长皮椅、木板墙、百叶窗、明亮的桌布及制服，是典型的俱乐部式扒房。蟹肉饼、牛肉他他、龙虾、生蚝……食材全由美国进口。优质的食材，虽经长时间运送，但品质不光没受影响，在厨师精湛的厨艺下更是美味可口。优秀的烹调功夫，要论本地优秀扒房，这间餐馆必是其一。

TEL. 8125 5256
22 Gemmill Lane
仁美巷22号
www.lukes.com.sg

■ **PRICE** 价钱
Lunch 午膳
à la carte 点菜 $ 85-180
Dinner 晚膳
à la carte 点菜 $ 85-180

■ **OPENING HOURS** 营业时间
Lunch 午膳 12:00-14:30 (L.O.)
Dinner 晚膳 17:00-23:45 (L.O.)
Thursday to Saturaday 周四至周六
12:00-23:45 (L.O.)

■ **ANNUAL AND WEEKLY CLOSING**
休息日期
Closed 1 day Lunar New Year and Sunday 农历新年1天及周日休息

♿ 🅿 🍽 ⊘🍴

TEL. 6684 5054

Suntec City Mall Tower 2,
#03-314, 3 Temasek Boulevard

淡马锡林荫道3号
新达城广场Tower 2 #03-314

magurodonya.com

■ **PRICE 价钱**
Lunch 午膳
set 套餐 $ 19-80
à la carte 点菜 $ 30-145
Dinner 晚膳
set 套餐 $ 19-80
à la carte 点菜 $ 30-145

■ **OPENING HOURS 营业时间**
Lunch 午膳 11:30-14:00 (L.O.)
Dinner 晚膳 17:30-22:00 (L.O.)

■ **ANNUAL AND WEEKLY CLOSING**
休息日期
Closed Lunar New Year eve to 2nd
day of Lunar New Year
农历新年除夕至初二休息

🍴⭕

MAGURO-DONYA MIURA-MISAKI-KOU
三浦三崎港

Japanese • Cosy
日本菜 • 舒适

If you want to enjoy tuna, then trusting in one of Japan's established tuna wholesalers is a sensible move. Trained fishermen, well established storage procedures and an in-depth knowledge of the species itself all help ensure that the quality is always high and that the prices are kept competitive. As well as cuts not often found in Japanese restaurants are specialities like grilled maguro collar and minced extra fatty maguro.

由日本一家鲔鱼供应商营运,鲔鱼的素质有一定保证。店内八成材料每周三次由日本直送而来,保存于零下六十度的冰箱,确保鱼类新鲜。师傅专业而独特的切鱼手法,使鱼生的口感特佳,在别处绝对吃不到。除招牌菜烧鲔鱼鱼鲛及免治特级油香鲔鱼外,还可选择厚切大腹或其他罕有部位,如Toumi或Kamatoro刺身。

MAJESTIC
大華

Cantonese • Modern
粤菜 • 现代

Reopened in 2018 at this location, the airy dining room sits under a glass roof and overlooks a garden. The food combines modern techniques with time honoured traditions and is exquisite in both taste and appearance. Try their dim sum, Hor-fun noodles made in house or Hakka ginger wine chicken soup with no water added. Business diners can opt for items in individual servings. Reservations a week ahead are recommended.

从酒店迁至现址的时尚商业大楼内，独特的环境设计和人工庭园让餐厅倍添时尚气息，在此品尝传统却口味新鲜的精致粤菜实是赏心乐事。推介原汁原味、不加水制作的客家姜酒鸡煲，厨师手拉河粉也值得一试。选址商业区，餐厅为菜单作特别安排，不少菜式以一人为上菜单位，方便商务客人。座位不多，建议提前一星期预订。

& P ⇔10 Ⓒ📶

TEL. 6250 1988

**Marina One,
The Heart (East Tower), #04-01
5 Straits View**

海峡林景5号
滨海盛景 The Heart #04-01

www.restaurantmajestic.com

■ **PRICE** 价钱
Lunch 午膳
à la carte 点菜 $ 40-100
Dinner 晚膳
à la carte 点菜 $ 80-120

■ **OPENING HOURS** 营业时间
Lunch 午膳 11:30-14:30 (L.O.)
Dinner 晚膳 17:45-21:30 (L.O.)

CENTRAL 中区

CENTRAL 中区

 ♿ 🅿 ⇄40 ©❚

TEL. 6825 1008

**InterContinental Hotel, Level 2,
80 Middle Road**
密驼路80号洲际酒店2层

manfuyuan.sg

■ **PRICE 价钱**
Lunch 午膳
set 套餐 $ 48-78
à la carte 点菜 $ 50-200
Dinner 晚膳
set 套餐 $ 78-98
à la carte 点菜 $ 50-200

■ **OPENING HOURS 营业时间**
Lunch 午膳 11:45-14:30 (L.O.)
Dinner 晚膳 18:30-22:00 (L.O.)

🍴○

MAN FU YUAN
满福苑

Cantonese • Elegant
粤菜 • 典雅

A comfortable space, professional service and a fairly priced menu combine to make this Cantonese restaurant, within the InterContinental hotel, a good choice. The kitchen brigade has remained unchanged for a long time and is celebrated for a number of its dishes: double-boiled black chicken soup with fish maw and conch; tea-smoked duck; and roasted suckling pig, for which two day's notice is required – the seafood is also always a popular choice.

厨房团队由经验丰富的香港主厨领导。花胶海螺炖鸡汤、樟茶鸭、烧乳猪及海鲜都是这儿无人不晓的名菜。装潢方面，以木地板、米色墙身、中式摆设及柔和的灯光作布置，感觉舒适自然。价钱相宜，侍应的服务态度也专业，是一间不错的粤菜馆。

MELLBEN SEAFOOD (ANG MO KIO)
龍海鮮螃蟹王 (宏茂桥)

Seafood · Neighbourhood
海鲜·亲切

It may not be in the most convenient location but that doesn't deter the crowds from descending on this open-air space. Nearly everyone is here for one thing: crab. The chef has 15 different ways to cook them, from black pepper crab to creamy butter crab and that, of course, includes the classic chilli crab. There's also live seafood available, along with Cze Char dishes – and the claypot bee hoon soup is delicious.

这里颇受本地人欢迎。晚市设开放式餐室，虽无空调但轻松随意。墙上挂满名人食客签名的螃蟹，鲜艳别致。招牌菜是螃蟹，菜单有多达十五种烹煮方式，除经典的辣椒蟹、黑胡椒蟹和牛油蟹外，不妨试试砂煲螃蟹米粉汤，非常鲜美。也供应每天到货的海鲜和各式本地煮炒菜式。星期六、日及假期不设订座。

TEL. 6285 6762
**Blk 232, #01-1222,
Ang Mo Kio Avenue 3**
宏茂桥道3号232座#01-1222

■ **PRICE** 价钱
Dinner 晚膳
à la carte 点菜 $ 40-60

■ **OPENING HOURS** 营业时间
Dinner 晚膳 17:00-22:30 (L.O.)

■ **ANNUAL AND WEEKLY CLOSING**
休息日期
Closed 5 days Lunar New Year
农历新年休息5天

CENTRAL 中区

TEL. 6738 1234

**Grand Hyatt Hotel,
Mezzanine Level, 10 Scotts Road**
史各士路10号
君悦酒店Mezzanine层
www.singapore.grand.
hyattrestaurants.com

■ **PRICE 价钱**
Lunch 午膳
set 套餐 $ 35-108
à la carte 点菜 $ 80-200
Dinner 晚膳
à la carte 点菜 $ 80-200

■ **OPENING HOURS 营业时间**
Lunch 午膳 12:00-14:45 (L.O.)
Dinner 晚膳 18:00-22:15 (L.O.)
Friday & Saturday dinner
周五及周六晚膳 18:00-22:45 (L.O.)

MEZZA9
International · Contemporary
国际菜·时尚

When you know you want to eat but aren't sure what you want to eat, there's always Mezza9 at the Grand Hyatt. This large, attractive restaurant offers nine different 'dining experiences' from Thai to Japanese, grills to seafood – you can sit anywhere you like and order from any of the show kitchens. It also boasts an impressive selection of martinis and over 350 labels on the wine list. Sunday brunch is a veritable institution.

在这家供应国际菜式的餐厅，你能享受到目不暇给的环宇美食，九大开放式厨房提供中西佳肴、烧烤美食、海鲜、泰菜、寿司、甜点和美酒，尽情满足贪吃的味蕾。其中酒吧的马天尼选择于新加坡称冠。星期日的早午合餐供应香槟，门庭若市，即使全场有四百个座位亦座无虚席，建议预先订座。

MIN JIANG
岷江川菜馆
Chinese · Elegant
中国菜 · 典雅

The graceful and immaculately kept Min Jiang has been a celebrated part of Goodwood Park hotel since 1982. It's named after the Min River in Sichuan province and serves dishes from this region, along with Cantonese specialities. Highlights include crispy chicken, sautéed prawns with dried red chilli, hairy crab in season, and hot and sour soup. The restaurant is also well known for its very popular dim sum, served from trolleys at lunchtime.

这里能尝到各式受欢迎的川菜、粤菜和沪菜, 招牌菜包括金牌吊烧鸡、宫保虾球、酸辣汤及一系列健康素菜和大闸蟹, 午膳时间随点心车出现的广式点心亦不容错过。餐厅以木地板衬托色调柔和的典雅家具, 洋溢着现代东方韵味。爱于户外用餐之士可选择池畔旁的用餐区。设有私人厢房, 适合商务午餐。

TEL. 6730 1704
Goodwood Park Hotel,
22 Scotts Road
史各士路22号良木园酒店
www.goodwoodparkhotel.com

■ **PRICE** 价钱
Lunch 午膳
set 套餐 $ 38-98
à la carte 点菜 $ 40-200
Dinner 晚膳
set 套餐 $ 78-98
à la carte 点菜 $ 40-200

■ **OPENING HOURS** 营业时间
Lunch 午膳 11:30-14:00 (L.O.)
Dinner 晚膳 18:30-22:00 (L.O.)

CENTRAL 中区

♿ 🍽 ⚚12 🍽

TEL. 9834 9935

National Gallery Singapore, #02-01, 1 St. Andrew's Road (enter via Coleman Street entrance)

圣安德烈路1号国家美术馆#02-01（哥里门街入口）

www.violetoon.com

■ **PRICE** 价钱
Lunch 午膳
à la carte 点菜 $ 35-75
Dinner 晚膳
à la carte 点菜 $ 35-75

■ **OPENING HOURS** 营业时间
Lunch 午膳 12:00-14:30 (L.O.)
Dinner 晚膳 18:00-21:30 (L.O.)

🍴🍽

NATIONAL KITCHEN

Singaporean • Design
新加坡菜 • 型格

Art and sculptures aren't the only treasures found in the National Gallery – on the 2nd floor is this restaurant from Violet Oon, Singapore's own national treasure and one of its greatest ambassadors. The handsome, panelled 1920s-style dining room is an ideal backdrop to the cooking which, through its spicing, contrasting textures and enticing aromas, showcases Singapore's unique culinary heritage. This is a restaurant with genuine charm.

想停一停、歇一歇？娘惹菜代表人物Violet Oon这家充满殖民时期气息的餐厅是不二之选。马赛克地台、串珠水晶吊灯、新加坡老照片、镶有镜子的黑木墙，室内环境高雅迷人。菜式如五香肉卷、小金杯、冷当牛肉、印尼黑果焖鸡等，从调味、层次和香气方面，充分呈现了娘惹菜的独特风味。千万别错过木薯糕。

🍴○

NICOLAS

French • Classic

法国菜•经典

The eponymous French chef has been quietly going about his business in this comfy and intimate little restaurant for some years now. Choose the Tasting menu to best experience his cooking skills which are ruddered by classical French techniques and rely on top quality ingredients, like langoustines from New Zealand and pigeon from Brittany.

名称源自法籍东主兼主厨,餐厅已扎根狮城十一年。店内有二十个座位和厨房旁的主厨餐桌,气氛温馨舒适,厨师执着于选用最佳食材,故不难看到来自新西兰的小龙虾或法国西北部的鸽子。上乘的材料加上正宗不花巧的烹调方法,成就了经典可口的法国菜肴。品尝菜单(Tasting Menu)充分展现主厨的烹饪造艺。

♨ 🅿 ⇆6 🍴
TEL. 6224 2404
10 Teck Lim Road
德霖路10号
www.restaurantnicolas.com

■ **PRICE** 价钱
Lunch 午膳
set 套餐 $ 42-68
Dinner 晚膳
set 套餐 $ 78-118

■ **OPENING HOURS** 营业时间
Lunch 午膳 12:00-13:30 (L.O.)
Dinner 晚膳 18:30-21:30 (L.O.)

■ **ANNUAL AND WEEKLY CLOSING**
休息日期
Closed Saturday lunch, Sunday and Monday 周六午膳、周日及周一休息

CENTRAL 中区

TEL. 6604 7050

**Marina Bay Financial Centre Tower 3,
#01-05, 12 Marina Boulevard**

滨海林荫道12号
滨海湾金融中心第三座#01-05

www.olarestaurant.sg

■ **PRICE** 价钱
Lunch 午膳
set 套餐 $ 29
à la carte 点菜 $ 60-120
Dinner 晚膳
à la carte 点菜 $ 60-120

■ **OPENING HOURS** 营业时间
Lunch 午膳 11:30-14:00 (L.O.)
Dinner 晚膳 17:30-22:00 (L.O.)

■ **ANNUAL AND WEEKLY CLOSING**
休息日期
Closed Saturday lunch, Sunday and
Public Holidays
周六午膳、周日及公众假期休息

OLA COCINA DEL MAR

Spanish • Industrial
西班牙菜 • 工业风

You'll often find this large and lively Spanish restaurant full of business types from surrounding offices, whether celebrating or commiserating after a day's work. The chef has worked with some big names but here the emphasis is on casual dining and simpler food. Along with the paella, the juicy and tender suckling pig is well worth ordering. The Peruvian-born chef also brings along some specialities from home, like ceviche.

工业风的设计风格，随意而时尚，不少白领下班后会来这儿点碟小吃和一杯西班牙酒放松一下。曾于专营高级菜的知名餐厅工作的主厨，以平凡和大众化形式演绎食材，让优质美食更普及。即席烤的乳猪，肉质鲜嫩、外皮松脆、油脂均衡；腌鱼炖饭融汇了青柠、辣椒和洋葱的辛香辣味，带有秘鲁风味。

OSTERIA ART

Italian · Intimate
意大利菜·亲密

This well-dressed restaurant is operated by Il Lido Group (see Aura and Braci) and provides a touch of sophistication to accompany its Italian food. The kitchen adds some smart modern touches to classic dishes; specialities include tagliolini with crab and Pachino tomatoes; pappardelle with pork cheek and red wine; and rack of lamb with eggplant. A warm and welcoming bar leads into the restaurant which boasts a 1930s New York Italian vibe.

由Il Lido集团经营的餐厅，供应的是带点现代风味的意大利菜式，每道菜式都经过精心处理，美味而地道，令你仿如置身意大利。招牌菜包括番茄蟹肉宽面条、猪颊肉宽蛋面、芦笋牛肉片及橄榄汁茄子羊架。餐酒单上能找到来自意法两国的美酒。

TEL. 6877 6933
55 Market Street
马吉街55号
www.osteriaart.com

■ **PRICE** 价钱
Lunch 午膳
set 套餐 $ 48
à la carte 点菜 $ 65-145
Dinner 晚膳
set 套餐 $ 108
à la carte 点菜 $ 65-145

■ **OPENING HOURS** 营业时间
Lunch 午膳 12:00-14:30 (L.O.)
Dinner 晚膳 18:30-22:30 (L.O.)

■ **ANNUAL AND WEEKLY CLOSING**
休息日期
Closed Saturday lunch, Sunday and Public Holidays
周六午膳、周日及公众假期休息

CENTRAL 中区

CENTRAL 中区

🔆 ⇔30 ⓞ❙ 🎎

TEL. 6227 6819

#01-02/03, 32 Maxwell Road
麦士威路32号#01-02/03
www.ottoristorante.com.sg

■ **PRICE** 价钱
Lunch 午膳
set 套餐 $ 38-138
à la carte 点菜 $ 70-120
Dinner 晚膳
set 套餐 $ 98-138
à la carte 点菜 $ 70-120

■ **OPENING HOURS** 营业时间
Lunch 午膳 12:00-14:30 (L.O.)
Dinner 晚膳 18:30-22:30 (L.O.)

■ **ANNUAL AND WEEKLY CLOSING**
休息日期
Closed Saturday & Public Holidays
lunch and Sunday
周六及公众假期午膳;周日休息

🍽️

OTTO

Italian • Contemporary
意大利菜 • 时尚

Authentic and recognisable dishes from across Italy draw plenty of customers to this well-regarded, well-established and comfortable Italian restaurant that's proven a good fit with the CBD. The various pasta dishes are not to be missed, as are the ossobuco and suckling pig; a truffle menu is offered in season and the lunch menu is great value. To accompany it all is a well-chosen wine list sourced entirely from Italy.

位处中央商业区,时尚具气派的装潢,邀约合作伙伴到此聚餐也不失礼。然而,公事其次,品尝美食才是重点。意国厨师烹调的经典意大利菜风味正宗,炖小牛肘、烤乳猪、卡帕奇奥牛肉等不可不试。在特定的季节里,会推出一些特别餐单如松露菜式。美酒配佳肴,这儿供应的红酒全部从意大利进口,品质俱佳。

🍴

POLLEN

European contemporary • Contemporary
时尚欧陆菜 • 时尚

Lunch is perhaps the best time for the green-fingered to visit this restaurant tucked away in the corner of the Flower Dome – not only to appreciate the bright, glass-enclosed room and the Mediterranean garden but also because you get a good value set menu and free entry to the world's largest greenhouse afterwards. The European menu displays a number of influences and the kitchen uses plenty of modern techniques; dessert is a highlight.

餐单包罗各款你能想到的时尚欧陆菜，菜式带有强烈的现代烹调风格，甚至会发现一些组合较特别的菜式，但以简单菜式和烤肉菜式为佳。午市套餐实惠而美味，能感受到厨师的造诣与热情。别忘了预留空间给滋味与创意并重的甜点啊！穿着土褐色外套的侍应生，服务很贴心。

♿ 🅿 📵

TEL. 6604 9988

**Flower Dome, #01-09,
Gardens by The Bay,
18 Marina Gardens Drive**

滨海花园通道18号
滨海湾花园花穹#01-09

www.pollen.com.sg

■ **PRICE 价钱**
Lunch 午膳
set 套餐 $ 55-85
à la carte 点菜 $ 90-200
Dinner 晚膳
set 套餐 $ 118-155
à la carte 点菜 $ 90-200

■ **OPENING HOURS 营业时间**
Lunch 午膳 12:00-14:30 (L.O.)
Dinner 晚膳 18:00-21:30 (L.O.)

■ **ANNUAL AND WEEKLY CLOSING**
休息日期
Closed Tuesday 周二休息

CENTRAL 中区

🏷 ♿ 🍷 **P** 🚗18 🍴

TEL. 6333 1788

**Pan Pacific Hotel, Level 3,
7 Raffles Boulevard**

莱佛士林荫道7号
泛太平洋大酒店3层

www.rangmahal.com.sg

■ **PRICE** 价钱
Lunch 午膳
set 套餐 $ 50-80
à la carte 点菜 $ 70-160
Dinner 晚膳
set 套餐 $ 60-120
à la carte 点菜 $ 70-160

■ **OPENING HOURS** 营业时间
Lunch 午膳 12:00-14:00 (L.O.)
Dinner 晚膳 18:30-22:00 (L.O.)

■ **ANNUAL AND WEEKLY CLOSING**
休息日期
Closed Saturday lunch
周六午膳休息

🍴

RANG MAHAL

Indian • Exotic décor
印度菜 • 异国风情

If you want plush without the fuss, consider this Indian restaurant on Level 3 of the Pan Pacific hotel – the double-height dining room is tastefully furnished, comfortable and contemporary. At lunch go with the flow by joining the dozens of business people here for the impressively bounteous buffet; dinner is the time to investigate the à la carte menu. The kitchen displays a respectful knowledge of the vast repertoire of Pan-Indian cuisine.

餐厅以一条暗暗的走廊和下方透光的印度神像迎接食客，用餐区环境奢华时尚。每天的午膳时间，络绎不绝的上班族会在这里出现，为的是餐厅所供应的印度式自助餐，孟加拉咖喱鱼(Bengali fish curry)、印式羊肉香饭(lamb biryani)等源源不绝地上场，爱吃印度菜的你，可会蠢蠢欲动？

SHANG PALACE
香宫

Cantonese · Luxury
粤菜 · 豪华

This comfortable and graceful Cantonese restaurant within the Shangri-La hotel is designed to give the impression that you're 'dining in a Chinese garden'. Cantonese cuisine is the mainstay of the menu but there are also Shanghainese influences. Chef Mok, who joined the kitchen crew in 2017, reinvented the menu by adding some innovative twists. However, the traditional dishes are just as good.

获誉为狮城最高级食府之一，餐厅以花卉和中式庭园为装潢主题，散发浓浓的东方韵味。厨房团队由新加入的主厨莫师傅所带领，不但将海派元素揉合到粤菜菜中，更加入了一些配搭新颖的广东菜式，然而传统口味亦不容错过。服务周到，餐酒选择丰富，甚至包括中国的黄酒和烈酒。

TEL. 6213 4398

Shangri-La Hotel, Lobby Level, 22 Orange Grove Road
柑林路22号香格里拉酒店大堂楼层
www.shangri-la.com/singapore

■ **PRICE 价钱**
Lunch 午膳
set 套餐 $ 88-388
à la carte 点菜 $ 50-250
Dinner 晚膳
set 套餐 $ 88-388
à la carte 点菜 $ 50-250

■ **OPENING HOURS 营业时间**
Lunch 午膳 12:00-14:15 (L.O.)
Weekend & Public Holidays lunch
周末及公众假期午膳
11:00-14:45 (L.O.)
Dinner 晚膳 18:00-21:45 (L.O.)

CENTRAL 中区

🅿 ♿6 🍴 ⚙

TEL. 6338 3788

The Ritz-Carlton, Millenia,
#03-01/02, 7 Raffles Avenue

莱佛士道7号
丽思卡尔顿美年酒店#03-01/02

www.shiraishi.sg

■ **PRICE 价钱**
Lunch 午膳
set 套餐 $ 40-130
à la carte 点菜 $ 100-250
Dinner 晚膳
set 套餐 $ 100-400
à la carte 点菜 $ 100-250

■ **OPENING HOURS 营业时间**
Lunch 午膳 12:00-14:00 (L.O.)
Dinner 晚膳 18:00-22:00 (L.O.)

■ **ANNUAL AND WEEKLY CLOSING**
休息日期
Closed 6 days Lunar New Year
农历新年休息6天

🍴○

SHIRAISHI
白石
Sushi • Simple
寿司 • 简朴

Concealed in the shadows of the Ritz-Carlton hotel is this serene sushi restaurant with a counter so soft it feels like velvet. The eponymous chef is chatty yet intense in his demeanour as he prepares the Edomae-style sushi, using fish flown in from Tokyo's Tsukiji Market. There are a number of menu options but it's best to leave yourself in his hands with the omakase, where equal care and attention goes into every dish.

餐厅藏身于丽思卡尔顿美年酒店内，位置隐蔽，但值得花时间寻找。热情而健谈的主厨在金黄色的长木桌后招待食客，这里提供的是传统江户前寿司，每件鱼生都经严格挑选，切割得恰到好处，连主菜外的味噌汤或前菜素质都叫人喜不自胜。有多种套餐选择，但建议交由厨师发办。

CENTRAL 中区

SIN HOI SAI (TIONG BAHRU)
新海山 (中峇鲁)

Seafood • Simple
海鲜 • 简朴

Located in a residential area and with over 30 years of history is this well-known seafood restaurant. On offer is live seafood only, from fish to shellfish – customers choose what they want from the tank. Don't miss the famous local choices of chilli crab and black pepper crab; the local Cze Char dishes are also good. You can sit inside or outside – the latter is the more atmospheric and relaxing area.

这家饭馆拥有逾三十年历史，位于住宅区内、在两幢楼房的地面层，室内室外均设有桌椅，室外的用餐区气氛较轻松自在。食物方面，此店以鲜活海鲜炮制的菜式驰名，食客可直接从水缸中挑选喜欢的海鲜。当然，别错过本地名菜辣椒蟹和黑胡椒蟹。还有地道的煮炒小菜供应。

TEL. 6223 0810
Blk 55, #01-59, Tiong Bahru Road
中峇鲁路55座#01-59

■ **PRICE** 价钱
Dinner 晚膳
à la carte 点菜 $ 30-60

■ **OPENING HOURS** 营业时间
Dinner 晚膳
17:00-04:00 (L.O.)

CENTRAL 中区

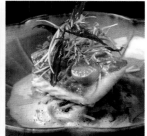

TEL. 6688 9955

Marina Bay Sands Hotel, Tower 2, Level 57, 10 Bayfront Avenue

贝弗兰道10号
金沙酒店二号塔楼57层

www.marinabaysands.com

■ **PRICE** 价钱
à la carte 点菜 $ 50-100

■ **OPENING HOURS** 营业时间
12:00-22:00 (L.O.)
Friday & Saturday 周五及周六
12:00-23:30 (L.O.)

SPAGO
Californian • Elegant
加州菜 • 典雅

Few restaurants are associated with a city more than Spago and LA, but to experience Wolfgang Puck's Californian cuisine you can now just head to Marina Bay Sands. The menu fuses European, Asian and American influences with clever tweaks and twists, in dishes like Big Eye tuna tartare cones and red snapper laksa. It's really two restaurants in one: a pool-side area for casual eating, and two elegant dining rooms for more ambitious dishes.

位处滨海湾金沙酒店顶层、著名的无边际泳池旁，有两条电梯可前往。池畔用餐区供应简餐，而坐拥迷人城景的室内用餐区供应的是高级精致的菜式。餐厅由美国厨师Wolfgang Puck主理，提供带亚洲和欧洲风味的加州菜，大眼鲔鱼他他卷(big eye tuna tartare cones)、香煎红鲷鱼叻沙及蜜糖味噌黑鳕鱼是招牌菜。

STRAITS CHINESE

Peranakan • Oriental décor

娘惹菜 • 东方

The owner's family opened Singapore's first Peranakan restaurant in 1953 – this branch has been in the CBD since 2011. Ornaments and wooden furniture lend a Chinese aesthetic. The versatile menu features dishes made with local produce and lots of spices and herbs, all prepared using traditional Chinese cooking methods. Dishes to try include Ayam Buah Keluak (chicken with local nuts) and Ikan Assam Nanas Pedas (sweet and sour fish).

店东家族是本地娘惹餐馆的始祖，其餐厅早于1953年开业。这家位于中央商业区内的餐厅于2011年营业，内有大量中式木家具和摆设，洋溢着浓浓的东方色彩。菜单选择丰富，厨师以本地食材和大量香料，结合中国技艺煮出传统娘惹风味，味道丰富且具特色。推介以坚果和鸡肉煮成的黑果炆鸡(Ayam Buah Keluak)和酸甜开胃的阿参凤梨酸辣鱼(Ikan Assam Nanas Pedas)。

30

TEL. 6225 8683

Keck Seng Tower, #B1-01,
133 Cecil Street
丝丝街133号激成大厦#B1-01
www.straitschinese.com

■ PRICE 价钱
Lunch 午膳
set 套餐 $ 12
à la carte 点菜 $ 25-35
Dinner 晚膳
à la carte 点菜 $ 25-35

■ OPENING HOURS 营业时间
Lunch 午膳 11:30-14:30 (L.O.)
Dinner 晚膳 18:00-21:30 (L.O.)

🍽22 ◎🍴

TEL. 6733 3333

**Tanglin Shopping Centre,
#04-10/13, 19 Tanglin Road**

东陵路19号
东陵购物中心#04-10/13

www.tambuahmas.com.sg

■ **PRICE** 价钱
à la carte 点菜 $ 25-40

■ **OPENING HOURS** 营业时间
11:00-21:30 (L.O.)

■ **ANNUAL AND WEEKLY CLOSING**
休息日期
Closed 3 days Lunar New Year and
1 day Hari Raya Aidilfitri
农历新年3天及开斋节1天休息

🍴○

TAMBUAH MAS (TANGLIN)

Indonesian • Simple
印尼菜 • 简朴

Founded in 1981, Tambuah Mas specialises in Indonesian home-style cuisine from Padang, Sulawesi, and Java. The look has remained largely unchanged over the years but no one is here for the décor – they come for dishes like rendang lembu (braised beef in spice and coconut milk); tahu telor (fried cubed beancurd and egg) and kepala ikan istimewa (fish head simmered in tangy spicy sweet and sour asam sauce). The menu is not overlong and the dishes are full of flavour and nicely balanced.

餐厅于1981年开业，吸引食客的并非多年来不变的木餐桌和绿色藤椅，而是餐厅所炮制的印尼巴东菜。餐单选择不算丰富，以巴东经典菜式为主，用料简单但每一道都富含味道，酱汁多加入椰汁以中和辣味。招牌菜有仁当咖喱、鸡蛋炒豆腐粒及阿参鱼头。十人以上可点选套餐。

TERRA

Italian · Contemporary
意大利菜·时尚

The food is Italian so don't get confused by the 'Tokyo-Italian' strapline – it refers to the two countries' shared respect for seasonal ingredients. To fully experience the considerable skills of Tokyo-born chef-owner Seita Nakahara it's best to have his 'omakase' menu which may include his homemade bottarga with Hokkaido sea urchin and spaghetti, or roasted scallops with vegetables. The dining room is equally pleasing on the eye.

餐厅标榜"东京意大利"令人对其菜式产生疑窦,其实是曾在意国工作的年青主厨Seita Nakahara希望将两地对食材的敬重融合在菜式上,食材均来自日本和意大利。多种元素构成满是惊喜的厨师发办餐单,如海胆金枪鱼子手造意大利面,烹调方法简朴却溢满滋味。常到世界各地餐室考察的主厨对烹饪的热诚可谓不言而喻。

🍴6 🚕 ⏱️🍴
TEL. 6221 5159
#01-01, 54 Tras Street
道拉实街54号#01-01
www.terraseita.com

■ **PRICE 价钱**
Lunch 午膳
set 套餐 $ 42-128
Dinner 晚膳
set 套餐 $ 168-308

■ **OPENING HOURS 营业时间**
Lunch 午膳 12:00-13:30 (L.O.)
Dinner 晚膳 18:30-21:30 (L.O.)

■ **ANNUAL AND WEEKLY CLOSING**
休息日期
Closed Saturday lunch, Sunday and Public Holidays
周六午膳、周日及公众假期休息

CENTRAL 中区

141

CENTRAL 中区

♿ ⛲ ⪡ ♨ 🅿 🍴

TEL. 6597 5266

**The Fullerton Bay Hotel,
80 Collyer Quay**

哥烈码头80号富丽敦海湾酒店

fullertonbayhotel.com

■ **PRICE 价钱**
Lunch 午膳
set 套餐 $ 38-168
à la carte 点菜 $ 45-70
Dinner 晚膳
set 套餐 $ 58-69
à la carte 点菜 $ 45-70

■ **OPENING HOURS 营业时间**
Lunch 午膳 12:00-14:30 (L.O.)
Weekend & Public Holidays lunch
周末及公众假期午膳
11:00-14:00 (L.O.)
Dinner 晚膳 18:30-22:00 (L.O.)
Weekend & Public Holidays dinner
周末及公众假期晚膳
18:30-22:30 (L.O.)

🍴

THE CLIFFORD PIER

Singaporean · Historic
新加坡菜·古典

A striking room and a wonderful setting make
this one of the more glamorous spots around.
The food honours the hawkers who once lined
the pier – head for the 'Heritage Signature'
dishes such as the Hainanese chicken rice
and the prawn laksa. There's also plenty on
offer for those not wanting to venture too far
outside their comfort zones, with dishes like
linguine alla vongole and lobster roll. Start with
a cocktail in the Landing Point Bar.

餐馆设于码头之上，港湾景色一览无遗，吸引无数游
人到此停驻，气氛亦因此而变得热闹。高高的拱型天
花、时尚中带点古典味的吊灯，令原已偌大的餐馆空
间更为广阔。独泊在一隅的黄包车，提醒食客这儿供
应的是传统新加坡美食如海南鸡饭和叻沙等。龙虾卷
及蛤蜊扁面条也别具风味。

THE DEMPSEY COOKHOUSE & BAR

European · Contemporary
欧陆菜 · 时尚

A place to see and to be seen, this restaurant in a heritage building targets the segment of the market somewhere between fine and casual dining. The elegant all-white interior pay homage to the city's colonial past. Besides signature dishes from the Jean-Georges group, new creations with an Asian twist are also served. Try its truffle fontina pizza from the cherry and apple wood oven, and its signature caviar selection. Reservations recommended.

作为Jean-Georges名下餐厅一员,這里高雅中不失随性,供应招牌菜但无碍厨师推陈出新,巧妙的平衡令此处出类拔萃。菜式种类多样,有其添加亚洲风味的拿手菜和各种鱼子酱,其中以樱桃及苹果木烤制的黑松露芝士薄饼大受欢迎。餐室设计简单高雅,加上位处文物建筑内,适合各种聚餐或举办私人活动,故宜提前订座。

♿ 🍽 **P** ⏎28 🍽

TEL. 1800 304 5588
Block 17D, Dempsey Road
登布西路17号D
www.jean-georges.com

■ **PRICE 价钱**
Lunch 午膳
set 套餐 $ 40-48
à la carte 点菜 $ 55-120
Dinner 晚膳
à la carte 点菜 $ 80-150

■ **OPENING HOURS 营业时间**
Lunch 午膳 12:00-14:30 (L.O.)
Weekend & Public Holidays lunch
周末及公众假期午膳
11:30-15:00 (L.O.)
Dinner 晚膳 18:00-22:00 (L.O.)
Friday, Saturday & eve of Public
Holidays dinner 周五、六及公众假期
前夕晚膳 18:00-23:00 (L.O.)

CENTRAL 中区

CENTRAL 中区

✦ ⛷ 🅿 🍴 ⚜

TEL. 6877 8140

**The Fullerton Hotel, Level 8,
1 Fullerton Square**

浮尔顿广场1号富丽敦酒店8层

www.fullertonhotels.com

■ **PRICE** 价钱
Lunch 午膳
set 套餐 $ 49
à la carte 点菜 $ 70-100
Dinner 晚膳
à la carte 点菜 $ 70-100

■ **OPENING HOURS** 营业时间
Lunch 午膳 12:00-14:30 (L.O.)
Dinner 晚膳 18:00-22:30 (L.O.)

■ **ANNUAL AND WEEKLY CLOSING**
休息日期
Closed Weekend lunch
周末午膳休息

🍽

THE LIGHTHOUSE

Italian • Elegant
意大利菜•典雅

Great views, warm service and Italian food –
for those looking for a romantic meal this is as
close to a sure thing as you can get. Be sure to
start with a drink on the rooftop to take in the
dramatic vista before moving inside to enjoy
the familiar Italian fare. The menu pays much
attention to the southern coastal regions;
the cooking eschews ostentation and instead
focuses on what is needed to make a particular
dish delicious.

甫步出电梯，映入眼帘的是亲切友善的笑容，若天公
造美不妨在入席前到顶层酒吧浅尝一杯，景色醉人。
餐厅供应的是质朴传统的意大利风味，在主厨严密的
监督下，菜式水准毋庸置疑。服务员知识丰富，大量
地道的意大利食材、迷人的景致，加起来就是一餐叫
人满足的意式盛宴。

Born naturally sparkling,
Badoit's fine bubbles subtly awaken
flavours of meals and fine wine.

Unique mineral composition and
pure as nature intended.

The perfect accompaniment
for fine dining.

TIAN TIAN FISHERMAN'S PIER SEAFOOD
天天渔港

Seafood · Traditional
海鲜·传统

Don't be put off by the garish advertising boards – just take a seat on the tidy terrace by the water and enjoy their fresh seafood. The family have been on the quay for over 20 years and Tian Tian is their most recent reinvention. Bamboo clams with garlic, salt and pepper king prawns, and sea bass Hong Kong style are among the popular choices. You can also pick from the live seafood tanks and choose your preferred cooking method.

东主家族在驳船码头经营逾二十载,与相邻的姊妹店相比,这儿的装潢摆设较富现代感,所在地段更优越。香蒜蒸竹蛏、避风塘大虾和港式蒸海鲈也值得一试;也可以从外面自购海产,请厨师炮制成你喜爱的风味。不要让俗艳的广告板破坏了雅兴,在新加坡河岸享受鲜活海产菜式绝对是赏心乐事!

TEL. 6534 1771

73-75 Boat Quay
驳船码头73-75号

■ **PRICE** 价钱
à la carte 点菜 $ 60-110

■ **OPENING HOURS** 营业时间
11:30-00:00 (L.O.)

CENTRAL 中区

CENTRAL 中区

⚇16 🍴 ☺🍴

TEL. 6475 2217

38 Tanjong Pagar Road
丹戎巴葛路38号
www.tipplingclub.com

■ **PRICE** 价钱
Lunch 午膳
set 套餐 $ 45-95
Dinner 晚膳
set 套餐 $ 170-270

■ **OPENING HOURS** 营业时间
Lunch 午膳 12:00-14:30 (L.O.)
Dinner 晚膳 18:00-22:00 (L.O.)

■ **ANNUAL AND WEEKLY CLOSING**
休息日期
Closed Saturday lunch and Sunday
周六午膳及周日休息

🍴⚊🍴

TIPPLING CLUB

Innovative • Modern
创新菜•现代

Ryan Clift's discreetly signed flagship restaurant is dominated by a long kitchen counter, which is where most diners choose to sit so that they can engage with the chefs and watch them in action – lunch is a simpler affair so come for dinner to fully appreciate their ability and ambition. They embrace all the latest techniques to produce quite elaborate and exciting dishes with some challenging combinations of flavour and texture.

Ryan Clift魔下餐厅的旗舰店,以精细的烹调技术为立店之本。厨房团队紧贴烹饪潮流,采用最新烹调方式制作菜式,精致与创意兼备,为食客带来味觉与质感的冲击。长长的餐柜台让厨师的烹调过程一览无遗。邻房是环境舒适的酒吧,为客人提供多款实验鸡尾酒,要找一款合你口味的鸡尾酒并不困难。

TUNGLOK SIGNATURES (CLARKE QUAY)
同樂经典 (克拉码头)

Chinese • Classic
中国菜 • 经典

Good ingredients and authentic flavours make this Chinese restaurant a worthy choice if you're seeking sustenance in The Central shopping mall. It is one of four branches in Singapore and you can choose between Cantonese, Shanghainese and Sichuan dishes. Specialities include charcoal-grilled honey pork shoulder, and crisp fried Sakura chicken. It's a big, busy and keenly run restaurant, with outside tables that provide good views of Clarke Quay.

位处克拉码头地鉄站之上，晚膳时段可选择户外座位，饱览码头的醉人景致。餐厅有四家分店，其餐牌和供应的菜式一样绚烂夺目，在这里可尝到广东菜、上海菜和四川菜。上乘的食材、传统的风味融合厨师的时尚风格，带来讨人欢心的菜式，例如炭烧蜜汁猪肩肉、脆皮樱花鸡等等。服务殷勤友善。

🏠 ≼ ♿12

TEL. 6336 6022

**The Central, #02-88,
6 Eu Tong Sen Street**
余东旋街6号The Central#02-88
www.tungloksignatures.com

■ **PRICE** 价钱
Lunch 午膳
set 套餐 $ 58-98
à la carte 点菜 $ 30-50
Dinner 晚膳
set 套餐 $ 78-98
à la carte 点菜 $ 50-80

■ **OPENING HOURS** 营业时间
Lunch 午膳 11:30-14:30 (L.O.)
Dinner 晚膳 18:00-22:00 (L.O.)

CENTRAL 中区

♿24 ⚪🍴 ♿
TEL. 9776 2828
#01-01, 28 Wilkie Road
威基路#01-01
www.28wilkie.com

■ **PRICE 价钱**
Dinner 晚膳
set 套餐 $ 138
à la carte 点菜 $ 100-150

■ **OPENING HOURS 营业时间**
Dinner 晚膳 15:00-22:00 (L.O.)

■ **ANNUAL AND WEEKLY CLOSING**
休息日期
Closed Sunday 周日休息

🍴

28 WILKIE N

Italian contemporary • Contemporary
时尚意大利菜·时尚

The elegant and comfortable dining room was styled and designed by the owner's wife. It boasts its own brand of caviar from its own farm in China, and its own range of balsamic and olive oils; they also have an exclusive brand of Austrian vodka and an excellent selection of beer and wine. The signature dish from the Italian menu features wagyu dish using only meat from 26-month-old females for its extra tenderness. No corkage fee.

精益求精，也许就是店东对于鱼子酱的态度。于中国昆明自设养殖场确保品质，除了作为店内的食材，更作零售，品质优良可见一斑。鱼子酱外，餐厅内的其他细节也是一丝不苟。例如其意大利黑醋及橄榄油均从意国本地运至，和牛只选用二十六个月大的母牛，取其肉质细嫩。用餐环境优雅舒适，爱酒的店东更欢迎客人自携美酒而不收取开瓶费。

WAH LOK
華樂

Cantonese • Contemporary
粤菜•时尚

A loyal clientele have made this comfortable, classically decorated Cantonese restaurant their own. The chef was born in Guangzhou but really developed his culinary skills and honed his craft in Hong Kong. His Cantonese dishes range from banquet delicacies like abalone and bird's nest soup to seafood dishes such as steamed fish. There are also Guangdong roast meats, claypot dishes and home-style dishes like steamed minced pork with salted fish.

華樂是本地很受欢迎的粤菜馆之一，设于酒店主楼座内，设计富现代感的餐室非特别豪华却讨人欢喜。原籍广州的大厨于香港学艺，餐单提供种类繁多的广东菜，无论是宴席菜式如鲍鱼燕窝，海鲜菜式如蒸海鱼，以至别具风味的煲仔菜、广东烧味和家常菜式，都让你品尝到正宗的粤菜口味。

P ⇔36 ◐

TEL. 6311 8188

Carlton Hotel, 76 Bras Basah Road
勿拉士峇沙路76号卡尔登酒店
www.carltonhotel.sg

■ **PRICE** 价钱
Lunch 午膳
set 套餐 $ 58
à la carte 点菜 $ 50-120
Dinner 晚膳
à la carte 点菜 $ 50-120

■ **OPENING HOURS** 营业时间
Lunch 午膳 11:30-14:15 (L.O.)
Dinner 晚膳 18:30-22:00 (L.O.)

CENTRAL 中区

P ⛭12 🍴 ☾🍴
TEL. 6339 9448

Hangout@Mt Emily,
10A Upper Wilkie Road
威基路上段10A爱美丽山旅馆
www.wildrocket.com.sg

■ **PRICE 价钱**
Lunch 午膳
set 套餐 $ 28-120
à la carte 点菜 $ 65-75
Dinner 晚膳
set 套餐 $ 75-160
à la carte 点菜 $ 65-75

■ **OPENING HOURS 营业时间**
Lunch 午膳 12:00-14:30 (L.O.)
Dinner 晚膳 18:30-21:30 (L.O.)

■ **ANNUAL AND WEEKLY CLOSING**
休息日期
Closed Monday lunch and Sunday
周一午膳及周日休息

🍴○

WILD ROCKET

Innovative • Design
创新菜 • 型格

After spending a few years as a lawyer the owner-chef decided to follow his dream and open a restaurant. The result is this bright, modern room on a hill with a charming Japanese aesthetic. He describes his cooking as 'Mod Sin': this means he takes traditional Singaporean dishes and adds his own innovative touches and modern accents, whether they be Thai, Japanese or Italian. Go for the omakase menu to best experience his cooking, or try the freshly made pasta.

原是律师的店东兼主厨因着对烹饪的热诚而开设这餐厅，时尚的室内设计和周遭环境相当融和，落地大玻璃透入自然光，同时令窗外景色一览无遗。店东形容菜式为现代新加坡(Mod Sin)派系，将新加坡传统食物跟泰、日或意大利美食混合创新而成。以时令食材炮制的厨师发办套餐和鲜制意粉值得一试。

YAN TING
宴庭

Cantonese • Luxury
粤菜 • 豪华

Since the name translates as 'Imperial Court' it's no real surprise this is a very comfortable room, ideal for impressing visitors and friends. The extensive Cantonese menu focuses on traditional dishes, with specialities like braised supreme sea cucumber with corn broth; prawn and pumpkin soup; wok-fried lobster with XO sauce; and braised oxtail in a claypot. The small alcoves are popular with those wanting a more intimate dining experience.

和煦的色调、时尚典雅的布置和宽敞的扶手椅,都令这餐厅成为浪漫晚餐和商务午餐的上佳之选。这里提供经典的广东菜肴,餐单选择丰富,驰名菜式包括小米扣辽参、金粟烧汁煎带子、南瓜浓汤烩虾球、头抽煎羊肚菌鸡脯、红酒烩牛尾煲和宴庭XO酱龙虾炒饭。

TEL. 6506 6887

The St. Regis Hotel, Level 1U,
29 Tanglin Road
东陵路29号瑞吉酒店1-U层
www.yantingrestaurant.com

■ **PRICE 价钱**
Lunch 午膳
set 套餐 $ 55-238
à la carte 点菜 $ 50-240
Dinner 晚膳
set 套餐 $ 98-238
à la carte 点菜 $ 50-240

■ **OPENING HOURS 营业时间**
Lunch 午膳 12:00-14:30 (L.O.)
Weekend lunch 周末午膳
10:30-15:00 (L.O.)
Dinner 晚膳 18:30-22:30 (L.O.)

CENTRAL 中区

🪑 ⬳ 🍴20 🕐🍴 ♨️

TEL. 6509 1488

**Ocean Financial Centre, Level 43,
10 Collyer Quay**

哥烈码头10号海洋金融中心43层

www.zafferano.sg

■ **PRICE 价钱**
Lunch 午膳
set 套餐 $ 42-98
à la carte 点菜 $ 90-150
Dinner 晚膳
set 套餐 $ 98
à la carte 点菜 $ 90-150

■ **OPENING HOURS 营业时间**
Lunch 午膳 11:30-14:30 (L.O.)
Dinner 晚膳 17:30-22:00 (L.O.)
Thursday to Saturday dinner 周四至
周六晚膳 17:30-23:00 (L.O.)

■ **ANNUAL AND WEEKLY CLOSING**
休息日期
Closed Sunday 周日休息

🍴🍽️

ZAFFERANO

Italian · Modern
意大利菜·现代

This authentic Italian gem occupies a sizeable space on the 43rd floor of the Ocean Financial Centre and provides wonderful views to go with your Brunello. But it's not just the terrace that draws the crowds – the kitchen shows passion and flair in all it does. Standouts include creamy burrata pomodorini with Cutrera olive oil and the various pasta dishes, like paccheri with Canadian lobster claw and luscious tomato sauce.

这家意大利餐厅置身四十楼层以上，坐拥广阔迷人景致。菜式以传统、正宗方法炮制，滋味无穷，如经典的水牛乳酪罗勒番茄沙拉，材料和调味搭配恰到好处，尝罢仿佛置身意大利之中。自家制的招牌意大利面条如八爪鱼管状面、鳕鱼扁面和意式肉饺等深受食客喜爱。酒单提供多款Biondi Santi佳酿。

HAWKER CENTRES
熟食小贩中心

ABC Brickworks Market & Food Centre
ABC红砖巴刹及熟食中心

Blk 6 Jalan Bukit Merah 惹兰紅山大牌6

Opened in 1974, near to industrial and residential areas, it has almost 100 stalls and is one of the most popular hawker centres. It was the birthplace of the Archipelago Brewery Company and, in remembrance of the company, was named ABC market.

于1974年开业，ABC三个字是为了纪念其前身——Archipelago Brewery Company——首家本地酿酒厂。中心内的店子不到一百家，食物种类却蛮多元化。因邻近工业和住宅区，使她跻身最受欢迎的小贩中心之列，当然，令人垂涎的美食绝对是主因：一份香喷喷的印度煎饼，一碗无添加味精的老火汤，光想想已叫人馋涎欲滴。

AR ER SOUP
阿2老火汤

Offers 8 kinds of MSG-free long-boiled soups, served with pumpkin rice.

八款无添加味精的老火汤，可配特色金瓜饭。

STALL 铺 | #01-141 **PRICE** 价钱 | $ 4-7
OPENING HOURS 营业时间 | 11:00-14:00, 17:00-20:00
Sunday & Public Holidays 周日及公众假期 17:00-20:00
Closed Saturday 周六休息

TIONG BAHRU YI SHENG FRIED HOKKIEN PRAWN MEE
中峇鲁益生炒福建虾面

40 years' experience goes into the cooking of the prawn noodles, stir-fried with homemade broth. Homemade chili sauce is also tempting.

东主四十多年来以自家熬制的浓汤炒制虾面，配以自制辣椒酱，齿颊留香。

STALL 铺 | #01-13 **PRICE** 价钱 | $ 4-6
OPENING HOURS 营业时间 | 15:00-22:45
Closed Wednesday 周三休息

CENTRAL 中区

Y. R AHMAD

18 kinds of cooked-to-order roti prata and murtabak; mutton soup.

十八款即点即制印度煎饼、馅料煎饼和羊肉汤。

STALL 铺 | #01-10 **PRICE** 价钱 | $ 2-8
OPENING HOURS 营业时间 | 10:00-19:00

Albert Centre
雅柏中心

270 Queen Street 奎因街270号

What makes this centre one of the best? Certainly one of the reasons is the food. Its location in a heritage district and near a famous shopping mall could be another reason why it attracts so many visitors.

风味地道的罗惹、香热惹味的沙爹,阵阵食物香从楼内飘出,实在引人遐思!丰富多样的美食、独具名气的经典小吃店,成就了雅柏中心的卓越地位。地处充满历史感的亚巴街和奎因街交界,邻近多个著名景点如专门售卖便宜货品的武吉士中心,占尽地利之便,不难明白为何她成为最受欢迎的小贩中心之一。

AH SENG
亚成潮州肉脞面

Its handmade meat balls are made not only with meat but also cartilage and sinew, making them delicious. The house-made sauce is appetising.

各式潮州手打肉丸面,肉丸含软骨和筋,鲜美非常;特制的汁酸辣惹味。

STALL 铺 | #01-77 **PRICE** 价钱 | $ 3-5
OPENING HOURS 营业时间 | 07:00-19:00
Closed Saturday 周六休息

PONDOK MAKAN INDONESIA

Offers 6 kinds of dishes; the cooked-to-order mutton satay is worth a try.

只供应六款食物,现点现烤的羊肉沙爹值得一试。

STALL 铺 | #01-123 **PRICE** 价钱 | $ 3-6
OPENING HOURS 营业时间 | 07:00-19:00
Closed Saturday 周六休息

CENTRAL 中区

SINGAPORE FAMOUS ROJAK
新加坡啰惹

Run by the second generation of the family. Local-style salad with a special homemade sauce.

由第二代经营。以地瓜、油条等拌以特制酱料和花生制作的罗惹，风味独特。

STALL 铺 | #01-45　**PRICE** 价钱 | $ 3-5
OPENING HOURS 营业时间 | 12:00-20:30

Alexandra Village Food Centre
亞历山大村美食中心

Blk 120 Bukit Merah Lane　红山1巷大牌120

The centre was re-opened in 2010 after the upgrade from the HUP project. It's always crowded by students, local workers and nearby residents as it's surrounded by car workshops and HDB. Tourists also come here to try famous local dishes like claypot laksa or Shui Jing Pau.

经HUP计划翻新后于2010年12月重开的亚历山大村美食中心，邻近四周的不是车房便是公共房屋或设施，尽享地理上的便利。打工一族、学生或是附近住宅的街坊在午饭时、下课后或闲暇时都喜欢到这里闲逛或大快朵颐。中心内的名店名食多不胜数：砂煲叻沙、猪尾汤、潮州蒸粿……总有一款对你的口味。

DEPOT ROAD ZHEN SHAN MEI CLAYPOT LAKSA
德普路真善美驰名砂煲叻沙

Ask for claypot laksa with blood cockles and you'll find the soup much tastier.

可选择在叻沙中加入鲜蛳蚶，味道更鲜美。

STALL 铺 | #01-75　**PRICE** 价钱 | $ 4-6
OPENING HOURS 营业时间 | 09:00-16:00
Closed Sunday　周日休息

HONG KONG YUMMY SOUP
真之味香港靓汤

Offers six kinds of soup, like lotus root pork ribs & winter melon pork rib. Also try steamed pork patty with pumpkin or steamed spare ribs.

供应莲藕排骨汤、冬瓜排骨汤、巴西蘑菇雪耳鸡腿汤等六款汤水，还有金瓜蒸肉饼和蒸排骨。

STALL 铺 | #01-51　**PRICE** 价钱 | $ 4-5
OPENING HOURS 营业时间 | 12:00-20:30
Closed Weekends & Public Holidays　周末及公众假期休息

🍴

LEON KEE CLAYPOT PORK RIB SOUP
諒記砂鍋當歸肉骨茶

The pork rib soup cooked with Chinese herbs is the signature dish; it also offers pig's tail soup and pork liver.

以中药材烹调的肉骨茶是招牌菜，此外亦有供应猪尾汤和猪肝等食物。

STALL 铺 | #01-18 **PRICE** 价钱 | $ 5-12
OPENING HOURS 营业时间 | 09:00-21:00,
Wednesday 周三 09:00-16:00

🍴

TIONG BAHRU LIEN FA SHUI JING PAU
中峇鲁联发水晶包

Teochew dumplings with jicama filling; also dumplings with red bean paste or taro paste after 1pm.

除了传统的沙葛馅潮州蒸粿外，下午一点后还供应红豆和芋泥馅的蒸粿。

STALL 铺 | #01-10 **PRICE** 价钱 | $ 1-3
OPENING HOURS 营业时间 | 08:30-15:00
Closed Sunday & Monday 周日及周一休息

🍴

XIANG JIANG SOYA SAUCE CHICKEN
香江豉油鸡

Along with the signature soya sauce chicken, it also offers other kinds of noodles like wonton noodles.

除了招牌豉油鸡外，还有云吞面类的面食供应。

STALL 铺 | #01-77 **PRICE** 价钱 | $ 3-18
OPENING HOURS 营业时间 | 08:00-14:30
Closed Tuesday 周二休息

CENTRAL 中区

Amoy Street Food Centre
厦门街熟食中心

7 Maxwell Road 麦士威路7号

Built in 1983, it has been renovated twice since. It's only 5-10 minutes from the MRT station and being near the CBD means that there are queues everywhere at lunchtime.

滋味香浓的卤面、馅丰味佳的肉粽、惹味香辣的咖喱鸡肉卜等驰名小吃,并不是令这幢建于1983年曾先后历两次翻新的熟食中心人流络绎不绝的唯一原因。邻近中央商业区,距丹戎巴葛MRT站约五至十分钟步程,也是吸引在中央商业区工作的行政人员到此享用午餐的原因。价廉味美的食物和便利的地点,难怪如此受欢迎!

A NOODLE STORY
超好面

The stall has an interesting look and sells local, traditional noodles cooked in an innovative way.

以新颖烹调方式制作的本土面食,店面设计同样创新。

STALL 铺 | #01-39 **PRICE** 价钱 | $ 6-10
OPENING HOURS 营业时间 | 11:15-14:30, 17:30-19:30, Saturday 周六 10:30-13:30
Closed Sunday & Public Holidays 周日及公众假期休息

AH TER TEOCHEW FISH BALL NOODLES
传统潮州手工鱼圆香菇肉脞面

The robust flavour of the broth shows how long the meat and bones were boiled. The noodles are topped with various ingredients.

经营至今三代,鱼圆肉脞面汤汁以肉骨长时间熬制,配料丰富,味道香浓。

STALL 铺 | #01-14 **PRICE** 价钱 | $ 4-6
OPENING HOURS 营业时间 | 07:00-21:00, Saturday & Public Holidays 周六及公众假期 07:00-15:00
Closed Sunday 周日休息

CENTRAL 中区

CENTRAL 中区

HONG KEE BEEF NOODLE
桐記牛肉粿條

Has over 60 years of history. The tasty beef stock is cooked for 24 hours.

六十多年老字号，用作汤底的牛肉汤经二十四小时烹煮，喝一口即齿颊留香。

STALL 铺 | #01-42 **PRICE** 价钱 | $ 4-6
OPENING HOURS 营业时间 | 11:00-19:00
Closed Public Holidays 公众假期休息

HOO KEE BAK CHANG
和記肉粽

Glutinous rice mixed with salted duck egg yolk; pork and chestnut wrapped with bamboo leaf.

咸蛋黄、猪肉、栗子与糯米混合后，以竹叶包裹蒸煮，传统中国食品。

STALL 铺 | #01-18 **PRICE** 价钱 | $ 3-4
OPENING HOURS 营业时间 | 11:00-17:00
Closed Sunday & Public Holidays 周日及公众假期休息

J2 FAMOUS CRISPY CURRY PUFF
驰名香脆咖喱卜

Popular street food - the curry chicken puff and sardine puff are excellent.

很普及的街头小吃，但咖喱鸡肉卜和沙丁鱼卜甚是出色。

STALL 铺 | #01-21 **PRICE** 价钱 | $ 1-2
OPENING HOURS 营业时间 | 08:00-15:00
Closed Sunday & Public Holidays 周日及公众假期休息

YUAN CHUN FAMOUS LOR MEE
源春驰名卤麵

Typical local food with strong flavours.

味浓色深，很地道正宗的面食。

STALL 铺 | #02-80 **PRICE** 价钱 | $ 4-6
OPENING HOURS 营业时间 | 07:30-14:30
Closed Thursday & Friday 周四及周五休息

Ang Mo Kio 724 Food Centre
宏茂桥724座巴刹与熟食中心

Blk 724, Ang Mo Kio Avenue 6
宏茂桥6道大牌724

Thanks to its convenient location, this centre is always packed. It has 45 stalls offering a range of dishes to satisfy your tastebuds. The minced meat noodles are always worth trying.

交通便利，加上相宜的价格，令这中心经常人头涌涌。虽然只得四十五家店子，但绝对不会令你的味蕾失望，不妨试试这里的肉脞面，色香味俱全，且物超所值，会让你感到不枉此行。

🍴🍽

HUP HUP MINCED MEAT NOODLE
合合香菇肉脞麵

The Teochew minced meat is delicious.

潮式肉脞面配上两片炸脆了的云吞皮，口感丰富。

STALL 铺 | #01-39 **PRICE 价钱** | $ 3-5
OPENING HOURS 营业时间 | 11:00-20:00

CENTRAL 中区

Chinatown Complex Market & Food Centre
牛车水

335 Smith Street　史密斯街335号

Built in 1983 and upgraded in 2008 under the HUP project, this is the biggest centre in Singapore, with over 700 stalls, including 226 cooked food stalls, and comes with an authentic Chinese atmosphere.

兴建于1983年并于2008年透过HUP计划翻新过的牛车水，楼高五层，内有逾七百家店铺，当中包括二百二十六家熟食店，是现时新加坡最大的小贩中心。位处华人聚居地的中心地带，不论楼内楼外都是浓浓的中华文化气息。鸡油面、饺子、云吞……逛着看着，厨具碰撞声和扑鼻而来的灶香令肚子不禁饥肠辘辘。

CENTRAL 中区

ANN CHIN HAND MADE POPIAH
安珍手工薄餅

Popiah packed with ingredients including eggs, shrimps, carrot, peanuts etc. provide a rich and varied taste.

Popiah薄饼馅料丰富，有红萝卜、花生、鸡蛋和虾等，外皮软而味道具层次感。

STALL 铺｜#02-112　**PRICE** 价钱｜$ 2-3
OPENING HOURS 营业时间｜08:00-20:00

FATTY OX HK KITCHEN
肥牛過橋麵檔

Offers a wide array of noodles, including pork trotter and barbecue meats. The fresh yam noodles are handmade and for take away only.

提供多种面食，包括港式烧味、牛腩、水饺、猪手面，还有只限外卖的自制新鲜准山面。

STALL 铺｜#02-84　**PRICE** 价钱｜$ 3-20
OPENING HOURS 营业时间｜07:00-14:30
Closed Monday & Tuesday 周一及周二休息

LIAN HE BEN JI CLAYPOT
联合本记煲饭

The claypot rice comes with 3 options: assorted, preserved meat and chicken. Cooked-to-order with charcoal.

以炭火炮制瓦煲饭和汤,可选什锦饭、腊味饭和滑鸡饭,员工即场为客人烹调。

STALL 铺 | #02-198/199 **PRICE** 价钱 | $ 5-10
OPENING HOURS 营业时间 | 16:30-23:00
Closed Sunday 周日休息

LIAO FAN HONG KONG SOYA SAUCE CHICKEN RICE & NOODLE
了凡香港油鸡饭·面

Always a queue. Offers Cantonese soya sauce chicken and BBQ pork.

店外总看见排队的人龙。售卖粤式油鸡和叉烧。

STALL 铺 | #02-126 **PRICE** 价钱 | $ 3-14
OPENING HOURS 营业时间 | 10:30-15:30
Closed Wednesday 周三休息

168 CMY SATAY
168春满圆沙爹

Cooked-to-order satay with a tasty sauce.

即叫即烤肉串配美味酱汁;斑兰叶包饭团。

STALL 铺 | #02-168 **PRICE** 价钱 | $ 4-6
OPENING HOURS 营业时间 | 09:30-18:00

THE 50S
五十年代

The classic taste of Singapore: kaya toast with a cup of kopi kosong.

一客咖椰吐司、一杯黑咖啡,一份不变的星洲经典口味。

STALL 铺 | #02-048 **PRICE** 价钱 | $ 2-3
OPENING HOURS 营业时间 | 07:00-21:00
Closed Monday 周一休息

CENTRAL 中区

ZHONG GUO LA MIAN XIAO LONG BAO
中国拉面小笼包

Hand-pulled noodles; dumplings and Xiao Long Bao.

供应手拉面、云吞、饺子及小笼包。

STALL 铺 | #02-135 **PRICE** 价钱 | $ 3-6
OPENING HOURS 营业时间 | 11:30-21:00
Closed Monday & Tuesday 周一及周二休息

Golden Mile Food Centre
黄金熟食中心

505 Beach Road 美芝路505号

Situated below the Army Market, this centre was opened in 1975 to house resettled hawkers from the Jalan Sultan street market and has 111 stalls. You'll find hawkers with over 60 years of history and popular dishes like chilli mee, along with various vegetarian dishes.

于1975年开业，这里是为了安置另一市场的小贩而兴建，故中心内有不少历史悠久的店子。这里共有一百一十一家店子，提供地道辣椒面、虾面、叻沙、炒粿条，更能找到各式素食，诸如汉堡、沙爹、乌打、罗惹、素鸡饭等，菜香飘飘，彷若是素食者的天堂。

CHUNG CHENG
崇正

Typical local food: chilli mee, prawn mee and laksa.

供应辣椒面、虾面及叻沙。

STALL 铺 | #01-59 **PRICE** 价钱 | $ 3-5
OPENING HOURS 营业时间 | 09:30-18:30
Closed Tuesday 周二休息

91 FRIED KWAY TEOW MEE
91翠绿炒粿條麵

The Kway Teow Mee fried with greens is good.

锅气十足的炒粿条，因加了炒青菜在粿条上，故名翠绿炒粿条。

STALL 铺 | #01-91 **PRICE** 价钱 | $ 3-5
OPENING HOURS 营业时间 | 10:00-19:00
Closed Monday 周一休息

CENTRAL 中区

167

Holland Drive Market & Food Centre
荷兰通道巴刹与熟食中心

44 Holland Drive 荷兰通道44号

Built in 1979, Holland Drive Market & Food Centre went through a ten-month facelift in 2013 under the HUP program. With more than 40 food stalls and seating for 660, you can enjoy a wide variety of value-for-money snacks and dishes.

早建于1979年的荷兰通道巴刹与熟食中心于2013年历经了为期十个月的翻新，设有超过六百个座位和四十家小贩，当中可找到各种各样物超所值的菜式，嫩滑的粿汁卤鸭饭、散发引人香气的即制瓦煲饭……都是食客络绎不绝的原因。

CHENG HENG KWAY CHAP AND BRAISED DUCK RICE
進興粿汁鹵鴨飯

Tender and richly-flavoured braised duck, together with smooth Kway Chap – a simple yet delicious lunch.

嫩滑而浓郁的卤鸭肉，配上幼滑的粿汁，是简单而美味的午餐。

STALL 铺 | #02-05 **PRICE** 价钱 | $ 4-6
OPENING HOURS 营业时间 | 06:30-14:30
Closed Thursday 周四休息

NEW LUCKY CLAYPOT RICE
新鴻運瓦煲飯

Cooked-to-order claypot rice. While waiting, try their long-boiled soups.

即叫即制瓦煲饭，香气四溢，等候时不妨一试其老火汤。

STALL 铺 | #02-19 **PRICE** 价钱 | $ 10-25
OPENING HOURS 营业时间 | 11:00-13:00, 17:00-20:00
Closed Wednesday 周三休息

RU JI KITCHEN
如記小厨

Pork noodles and the popular handmade fish ball noodles are the draw, either in soup or dried.

两个铺位分别售卖肉胜面及较受欢迎的鱼圆面，鱼圆是手工制，可选干拌或汤面。

STALL 铺 | #02-28/29 **PRICE** 价钱 | $ 3-5
OPENING HOURS 营业时间 | 07:00-13:00
Closed Monday 周一休息

CENTRAL 中区

Hong Lim Market and Food Centre
芳林巴刹与熟食中心

Blk 531A, Upper Cross Street
克罗士街上段大牌531A

Built in 1978 and renovated in 2009, this was the first hawker centre in the Chinatown area. The 104 stalls offer Bak Kut Teh, fruit juice Mee Siam, curry chicken noodles, fish head Bee Hoon, etc. Expect long queues during lunch hours.

兴建于1978年，这是牛车水区内第一家小贩中心。它于2009年曾经翻新，现时共有104家店子，游走其中，仿如置身美食大观园：肉骨茶、果汁米暹、咖喱鸡面、鱼头米粉等美食的香气扑鼻而来，难怪在午膳时间总会看见长长的人龙，想吃就得有点耐性了。

AH HENG CURRY CHICKEN BEE HOON MEE
亚王咖喱鸡米粉麵

Potato and tofu puffs curry soup served with rice noodles; Hainanese chicken; and sliced fish.

马铃薯豆卜咖喱汤可配米粉或面，拌以海南鸡及鱼片。

STALL 铺 | #02-57/58 **PRICE** 价钱 | $ 4-6
OPENING HOURS 营业时间 | 10:00-21:00,
Weekends & Public Holidays 周末及公众假期 08:00-21:00

AH HENG DUCK RICE
同济前阿興鴨飯

The taste of duck meat marries with the spice marinade, each boasting a rich flavour. Snacks like duck liver and dried tofu are also offered.

卤水味道复杂，又与鸭肉配搭得宜，无盖过鸭肉的鲜甜味。尚有鸭肝、卤蛋、豆干等小吃。

STALL 铺 | #02-64 **PRICE** 价钱 | $ 5-10
OPENING HOURS 营业时间 | 06:30-16:00
Closed Monday 周一休息

FAMOUS SUNGEI ROAD TRISHAW LAKSA
馳名结霜橋三輪車叻沙

The laksa is famous for its rich flavour. The fruit juice Mee Siam is the signature dish.

配料丰富汤底鲜美的叻沙非常受欢迎；首创的果汁米暹也蛮特别。

STALL 铺 | #02-66 **PRICE** 价钱 | $ 3-8
OPENING HOURS 营业时间 | 11:30-16:30
Closed Sunday 周日休息

HOKKIEN STREET BAK KUT TEH
福建街肉骨茶

The dark coloured Bak Kut Teh has a strong flavour. There's also pork knuckle, pork intestines and steamed fish.

福建肉骨茶色深而味浓；此外还有供应猪脚、大肠和蒸鱼。

STALL 铺 | #01-66 **PRICE** 价钱 | $ 5-30
OPENING HOURS 营业时间 | 09:00-19:00

JI JI WONTON NOODLE
基記麵家

Local wonton and noodle dishes like chicken feet noodle and Ipoh Sar Hor Fun.

口味地道的云吞面食如鸡脚面、怡保河粉。

STALL 铺 | #02-48/50 **PRICE** 价钱 | $ 5-30
OPENING HOURS 营业时间 | 09:00-19:00

CENTRAL 中区

OUTRAM PARK FRIED KWAY TEOW
歐南園炒粿條麵

The Kway Teow is fried with a dark sauce; you can add cockles to the noodles. Always a long queue.

炒河粉颜色很深，可加鲜蛳蚶，味道很地道。档口前常见人龙。

STALL 铺 | #02-17 **PRICE** 价钱 | $ 3-5
OPENING HOURS 营业时间 | 06:00-15:30
Closed Sunday & Public Holidays 周日及公众假期休息

TAI WAH PORK NOODLE
大華肉脞麵

Noodles served with soup; meat balls, dried fish and pork liver.

与汤汁混和的面条再配上肉丸、鱼干及鲜猪肝等，十分滋味。

STALL 铺 | #02-16 **PRICE** 价钱 | $ 5-8
OPENING HOURS 营业时间 | 07:30-19:30

Maxwell Food Centre
麦士威熟食中心

1 Kadayanallur Street 卡达耶那鲁街1号

This centre began life in 1935 and has become one of the most iconic hawker centres in the city. Most typical dishes can be found here, including Rojak, banana fritter and popiah.

早于1935年开业的麦士威熟食中心，已成为新加坡最具代表性的小贩中心，林林总总非吃不可的小贩美食尽在其中——香脆味甜的炸香蕉、炸芋头、炸凤梨和薄饼，当然少不了地道的罗惹。

LIM KEE (ORCHARD) BANANA FRITTERS
林記油炸芎蕉

Apart from the sweet banana fritter, it also offers taro fritters and pineapple fritters.
除了香甜味美的炸香蕉外，还有炸芋头和炸凤梨。

STALL 铺 | #01-61　**PRICE** 价钱 | $ 2-3
OPENING HOURS 营业时间 | 11:00-18:00

ROJAK · POPIAH & COCKLE
囉嗦 · 薄餅 · 鮮蛤

A clean and tidy stall with just three kinds of food. The popiah with egg, vermicelli and bean sprouts is very appealing.
整洁的小店只供应三款食物，除了包着粉丝、鸡蛋、豆芽、生菜等的薄饼外，还有罗惹和鲜蛤。

STALL 铺 | #01-56　**PRICE** 价钱 | $ 3-8
OPENING HOURS 营业时间 | 12:00-23:00

CENTRAL 中区

173

TIAN TIAN HAINANESE CHICKEN RICE
天天海南雞飯

Don't be surprised to see a long queue – their Hainanese chicken rice is hugely popular.

驰名海外的海南鸡饭店，店外常常有长长的人龙。

STALL 铺 | #01-10/11 **PRICE** 价钱 | $ 4-12
OPENING HOURS 营业时间 | 10:30-20:00
Closed Monday 周一休息

Mei Ling Market & Food Centre
美玲巴刹与熟食中心

159 Mei Chin Road　美景路159号

This two-storey building was renovated in 2009 and is now home to 47 stalls. Some of them were once at the Commonwealth Food Centre, which explains why there is such a high concentration of quality hawker stalls in this market.

这市场楼高两层，于2009年透过HUP计划翻新，现有47家店铺，当中不少来自另一小贩中心，故即使场内店子数量不多，叫人惊喜的店铺仍举目皆是。必尝美食包括粤式牛腩面、猪脚面……软硬恰到好处的面条，配上香浓肉汁，光是想想已叫人兴奋不已。

LAO JIE FANG
老街坊

Cantonese-style braised beef noodles; pig's trotter noodles and beef tendon noodles are pretty good.

粤式牛腩面、猪脚面及牛筋面甚为出色。

STALL 铺｜#02-15　**PRICE** 价钱｜$ 4-8
OPENING HOURS 营业时间｜08:00-14:00

SHI HUI YUAN
實惠園

Thin, smooth rice noodles and gravy - with chicken, duck or chicken feet toppings.

幼滑河粉拌入香浓肉汁，可选配鸡、鸭或凤爪等。

STALL 铺｜#02-33　**PRICE** 价钱｜$ 3-5
OPENING HOURS 营业时间｜08:00-14:00
Closed Monday to Wednesday　周一至周三休息

CENTRAL 中区

Newton Food Centre
纽顿熟食中心

500 Clemenceau Avenue North
克里门梭北道500号

Upgraded and reopened in 2006, this is considered by many as the best hawker centre in the city and is popular with both locals and tourists. There are many signature dishes in the centre, such as BBQ seafood and black pepper crab, so it can be challenging getting a seat during busy periods.

这中心于2006年经过翻新，被誉为全新加坡最佳的小贩中心，深得本地老饕或旅客喜爱，若有幸到访，记得品尝惹味的海鲜烧烤和沙爹、令人回味无穷的海南鸡，络绎不绝的食客致使场内一席难求。

AH GONG TRADITIONAL HAINANESE CHICKEN RICE
阿公正宗海南鸡饭

Heavenly Hainanese chicken served with chicken oil rice. One chicken feeds four. Set menus are available.

海南鸡配上鸡油饭令人回味无穷，一只足够四人享用，亦有套餐供应。

STALL 铺 | #01-57 **PRICE** 价钱 | $ 5-32
OPENING HOURS 营业时间 | 11:30-22:00

ALLIANCE SEAFOOD
聯合海鮮燒烤

BBQ seafood. Don't miss the chilli crab or the black pepper crab made using live crabs.

烧烤海鲜，以活蟹制作的辣椒炒蟹和黑胡椒蟹绝不可错过。

STALL 铺 | #01-27 **PRICE** 价钱 | $ 15-40
OPENING HOURS 营业时间 | 11:00-23:00

HENG
興

The owner has 50+ years' experience serving sweet or savoury carrot cakes. Fried oysters and oyster omelettes are also worth a try.

近五十年制糕经验,售卖甜及咸两种萝卜糕,蚝煎和蚝蛋也相当不错。

STALL 铺 | #01-28 **PRICE** 价钱 | $ 4-10
OPENING HOURS 营业时间 | 18:00-00:30

115 Bukit Merah View Market & Hawker Centre
红山景大牌115

Blk 115 Bukit Merah View 红山景大牌115

This hawker centre, opened in 1973, comprises 84 cooked food stalls and 167 market produce stalls. Located in the Henderson area and close to office buildings, schools and residential flats, the centre is always flooded with people thanks to its delicious, great value lunch choices.

这幢座落于红山区、建于1973年的小贩中心现有超过一百五十家商店和八十四家熟食小贩店，提供各式各样经济实惠的地道美食。由于四周尽是办公室、学校和住宅，午膳时间总是肩摩毂击。楼内飘来浓浓咖喱香，咖喱迷必能捧着肚子满足而回。

CHAI CHUAN TOU YANG ROU TANG
柴船头羊肉汤

It has mastered the art of cooking mutton, with dishes like mutton soup, mutton meatballs and mutton offal.

供应羊肉汤、羊肚、羊肉丸、羊脚筋和羊脑等。

STALL 铺 | #01-51 **PRICE** 价钱 | $ 3-8
OPENING HOURS 营业时间 | 11:00-14:30
Closed Sunday & Public Holidays 周日及公众假期休息

NA NA CURRY
南南咖喱

Curry fish; chicken, mutton and curry fish-head in claypots are delicious.

咖喱鱼、羊、鸡及砂锅咖喱鱼头很美味。

STALL 铺 | #01-47 **PRICE** 价钱 | $ 3-10
OPENING HOURS 营业时间 | 10:00-20:00
Closed Sunday 周日休息

127 Toa Payoh West Market & Food Centre
大巴窑大牌127

Blk 127, Lorong 1 Toa Payoh   大巴窑1巷大牌127

This small hawker centre consists of only 40 stalls, yet the food on offer is more than satisfying. One must-try item is the handmade Teochew pau - bite-sized and full of amazingly delicious fillings. The very tasty carrot cake is also worth having.

即使这中心只有四十家店子，还是值得远道而来。潮式包点是其中一种必尝美食，别看它个子小小，松软的包皮裹着各式诱人馅料，一口大小正好可多尝几款。而菜头粿亦值得一试，裹着蛋浆的菜头粿煎得外脆内软，一试难忘。

CENTRAL 中区

CHEY SUA CARROT CAKE
青山菜頭粿

The pan-fried cake is popular. They'll deliver the food to your table when there's no queue at the stall.

煎萝卜糕非常受欢迎。下单时报上桌子号码，店方会把食物送到你的桌上。

STALL 铺 | #02-30 **PRICE** 价钱 | $ 2-4
OPENING HOURS 营业时间 | 06:30-13:00
Closed Monday 周一休息

COME DAILY FRIED HOKKIEN PRAWN MEE
天天來炒福建虾面

Hokkien prawn mee made with egg noodles, rice vermicelli and seafood, topped with pork crackling.

以黄面和米粉配上海鲜的传统福建虾面，加上香脆的猪油渣，层次更丰富。

STALL 铺 | #02-27 **PRICE** 价钱 | $ 4-10
OPENING HOURS 营业时间 | 08:00-14:30
Closed Monday 周一休息

LAO SHEN JI SI MIAN
老沈雞絲麵

Offers hand-made noodles in soup with fish balls or fish dumplings; and noodles with mushroom or shredded chicken. You can order noodles with two toppings.

全手工制作的鱼圆面、鱼饺面、冬菇或鸡丝拌面，也可点选双拼。

STALL 铺 | #02-01　**PRICE** 价钱 | $ 3-5
OPENING HOURS 营业时间 | 07:00-13:30
Closed Monday 周一休息

TEOCHEW HANDMADE PAU
潮洲自制飽點

The lotus seed paste pau; steamed chicken pau; and Longevity pau are all handmade.

莲蓉包、大鸡包及寿桃包等潮式包点全部人手炮制。

STALL 铺 | #02-02　**PRICE** 价钱 | $ 2-3
OPENING HOURS 营业时间 | 06:00-14:00
Closed Monday 周一休息

CENTRAL 中区

Pek Kio Market & Food Centre
白桥巴刹熟食中心

41 Cambridge Road 剑桥路41号

Tucked behind the houses opposite KK Women's & Children's Hospital, this three-decades old centre is home to some devoted hawkers who inherited the stall from their parents. Though not easily accessible, it's worth a visit – come early as most sell out by late afternoon.

这熟食中心建于1984年，很多店子正由第二代继承，因此虽然交通不算便捷，还是得到不少老饕青睐，午膳时间更是人头涌涌。不少食物下午便售罄，不想扑空请预早前来。

PIN WEI HONG KONG STYLE CHEE CHEONG FUN
品味港式猪肠粉

Their rice roll is silky and has the perfect thickness. Different fillings, including scallop and abalone, are available.

肠粉皮滑溜且厚薄适中，并洒上芝麻；除了基本款式，还有带子肠、鲍鱼肠等供选择。

STALL 铺 | #01-25 **PRICE** 价钱 | $ 2-17
OPENING HOURS 营业时间 | 06:30-14:00
Closed Wednesday every two weeks 隔周于周三休息

SHENG SENG FRIED PRAWN NOODLE
生成炒虾麵

It's all about rice vermicelli and egg noodles stir-fried with eggs and seafood. Homemade chili sauce enriches the flavour.

油面、米粉以鸡蛋拌炒，加上海鲜配料，香气四溢。嗜辣者不妨试其带香甜味的特制辣椒酱。

STALL 铺 | #01-40 **PRICE** 价钱 | $ 3-5
OPENING HOURS 营业时间 | 10:00-15:00
Closed Monday 周一休息

CENTRAL 中区

WAH KEE BIG PRAWN NOODLES
華記大蝦麵

Their noodles, either in soups or dried, come with palm-sized prawns. Expect long queues.

手掌般大的虾，伴上干或汤面，吸引不少食客排队等候。

STALL 铺 | #01-15　**PRICE** 价钱 | $ 3-25
OPENING HOURS 营业时间 | 08:30-14:00
Closed Monday & Tuesday　周一及周二休息

People's Park Complex Food Centre
珍珠坊

32 New Market Road 纽马吉路32号

This two-level building is a favourite spot with local seniors and is conveniently located outside one of the entrances of Chinatown MRT Station.

随着饺子冒起的热腾腾蒸气、手拉面制作的即场展示、小笼包的丰腴肉香，交织出市场内人头涌涌的热闹画面。珍珠坊楼高两层，深受本地年长一辈喜爱。对旅客而言，此熟食中心内的食物不光价格相宜，且位处牛车水地铁站出口旁，是大快朵颐的便利之选。

🍴◯

HONG PENG LA MIAN XIAO LONG BAO
洪鹏拉面小籠包

Offers Xiao Long Bao, dumplings and hand-pulled noodles.

小笼包、饺子及即场制作的手工拉面。

STALL 铺 | #01-1016B **PRICE** 价钱 | $ 4-5
OPENING HOURS 营业时间 | 09:00-20:30

🍴◯

PEOPLE'S PARK HAINANESE CHICKEN RICE
珍珠坊海南雞飯/珍珠坊香港燒臘

Offers Cantonese roast meats, such as pork chop and duck; and, of course, the signature dish – Hainanese chicken rice.

各款粤式烧味如脆皮烧肉、叉烧、烧鸭等，当然，还有海南鸡饭。

STALL 铺 | #01-1098 **PRICE** 价钱 | $ 3-6
OPENING HOURS 营业时间 | 09:00-21:00

CENTRAL 中区

183

Tanjong Pagar Plaza Market & Food Centre
丹戎巴葛坊小贩中心

6 Tanjong Pagar Plaza 丹戎巴葛坊大牌6

Has been opened for 40 years, but this hawker centre had a facelift a few years ago. Located in the CBD and near the railway station, it's popular with workers in the district. Different kinds of food are offered, like Thai Tom Yam soup.

开业约四十年，数年前修缮重整完毕，此中心因其位置坐落金融区及邻近地铁站之便，吸引到大量于附近工作的人到此处用膳。中心内有不少种类的食品，诸如泰式的酸辣汤及咖喱。修葺后座位增加，空气更流通。

ISSAN THAI FOOD
泰国东北美食

Thai food like Tom Yam soup with rice, Phad Thai and green curry with rice is offered.

提供地道泰式食品如酸辣湯配飯、金边粉或青咖喱飯。

STALL 铺 | #02-13 **PRICE 价钱** | $ 5-10
OPENING HOURS 营业时间 | 11:30-15:00, 17:30-20:00, Saturday 周六 11:30-17:00
Closed Sunday 周日休息

ROLINA TRADITIONAL HAINANESE CURRY PUFF

Chicken curry and sardine puffs are too good to be missed.

主打鸡及沙丁鱼咖喱卜，不容错过。

STALL 铺 | #02-15 **PRICE 价钱** | $ 2-3
OPENING HOURS 营业时间 | 08:30-16:30

CENTRAL 中区

Tekka Centre
竹脚中心

665 Buffalo Road 巴弗罗路665号

This centre, in Little India, was originally named Zhujiao Centre. However, the word was too hard for non-Chinese locals to pronounce so it was renamed Tekka Centre in 2000. As it's a landmark in Little India, expect plenty of Indian fare.

竹脚中心位于小印度，外墙色彩斑烂，内有繁盛的香料市场，印度服饰和商品琳琅满目，洋溢着浓浓的印度风情。游走其中，你会找到口碑载道的印度香饭（黄姜饭），颗颗饭粒都渗着咖喱香气，搭配羊肉、鸡肉或鱼，吃得饱足；场内中式美食亦具水准，尤其推荐卤水鹅鸭。

🍴

ALLAUDDIN'S BRIYANI

The biryani is very famous; you may choose mutton, chicken or fish as a topping.

口碑载道的印度香饭，可选配羊肉、鸡肉或鱼等。

STALL 铺 | #01-229/232/233 **PRICE** 价钱 | $ 4-6
OPENING HOURS 营业时间 | 09:00-19:00

🍴

HENG GI GOOSE AND DUCK RICE
興記鵝·鴨飯

The soya sauce duck is very popular.

这儿的卤水鸭在区内很受欢迎。

STALL 铺 | #01-335 **PRICE** 价钱 | $ 4-10
OPENING HOURS 营业时间 | 08:00-14:30
Closed Monday 周一休息

Tiong Bahru Market
中峇鲁市场

30 Seng Poh Road 成保路30号

Located in one of the city's oldest residential areas, this market is one of the most popular hawker centres. There are so many great food items to choose from, like lor mee, prawn mee and roast chicken. The silky white Shui Kueh, topped with preserved radish and sauce, is very tempting.

坐落于新加坡最古老的住宅区,中峇鲁市场一直是本地人最爱的小贩中心,场内驰名美食不能尽录,卤面、虾面、烧鸡等等都香气四溢,而水粿由米浆蒸熟而成,佐以煎至咸香的菜脯粒和秘制酱汁,叫人垂涎欲滴。

CENTRAL 中区

HONG HENG FRIED SOTONG PRAWN MEE
鴻興炒蘇東蝦麵

Cooked-to-order, the noodles stir-fried with sliced fish, squid and prawn and served with homemade chilli sauce is a favourite.

即点即炒的油面加米线,配鱼片、鱿鱼、虾及秘制辣酱,带有浓浓虾膏咸香。

STALL 铺 | #02-01 **PRICE** 价钱 | $ 3-5
OPENING HOURS 营业时间 | 11:00-20:00
Closed Monday 周一休息

JIAN BO SHUI KUEH
榢柏水粿

Typical local street food: a white rice cake with preserved vegetables and a secret sauce.

雪白的米糕浇上秘制酱汁配以菜脯,很地道的街头小吃。

STALL 铺 | #02-05 **PRICE** 价钱 | $ 2-4
OPENING HOURS 营业时间 | 05:30-21:30

186

KOH BROTHER PIG'S ORGAN SOUP
許兄弟豬什湯

Provides a wide range of pork offal like liver, chitterlings and tripe.

各式的猪什如猪肝、猪肠、猪肚应有尽有。

STALL 铺 | #02-29 **PRICE** 价钱 | $ 4
OPENING HOURS 营业时间 | 08:30-15:30; 18:00-20:30
Closed Monday 周一休息

LOR MEE 178
鹵麵 178

Besides the Lor Mee, you should try the fish nuggets.

除了卤面，还可来一客炸鱼片。

STALL 铺 | #02-23 **PRICE** 价钱 | $ 3-4
OPENING HOURS 营业时间 | 07:00-14:00

TIONG BAHRU HAINANESE BONELESS CHICKEN RICE
中峇鲁海南起骨雞飯

Along with the signature Hainanese boneless chicken rice, it offers roasted chicken.

除了不容错过的镇店之宝——海南起骨鸡饭外，还供应烧鸡。

STALL 铺 | #02-82 **PRICE** 价钱 | $ 3-24
OPENING HOURS 营业时间 | 10:00-20:00
Closed Monday 周一休息

CENTRAL 中区

Whampoa Makan Place
黄埔熟食中心

91 Whampoa Drive 黄埔通道91号

There are 52 stalls housed between two blocks. Stalls in Block 91 mostly offer breakfast food and many close after lunch; stalls in Block 90 are usually open for lunch and dinner or even until midnight. A wide array of good food can be found here.

这市场只有五十多家店子,散布于两幢建筑内,其中91号的店以贩售早餐为主,午膳过后便会停业;而90号的店子主营午膳、晚膳,个别甚至营业至午夜。老饕可以在这里消磨一整天,从早餐的烤面包、粥,地道小吃蚝仔煎,以至令人捧着肚子的鲍鱼面和卤水鸭饭,总能满足你的胃口。

BALESTIER ROAD HOOVER ROJAK
豪華羅雜

Local-style salad with fresh ingredients; can be served with preserved duck egg.

以新鲜食材炮制的地道风味沙拉,可加皮蛋拌吃。

STALL 铺 | #01-06 **PRICE** 价钱 | $ 4-6
OPENING HOURS 营业时间 | 10:30-15:00
Closed Monday & Tuesday 周一及周二休息

BEACH ROAD FISH HEAD BEE HOON
美芝路魚头米粉

Specialises in fish dishes, various soups and sliced fish bee hoon. Tom Yam soup and fried fish soup is worth trying.

主营鱼片米粉,混搭不同汤品,除了特制的冬荫公汤,炸鱼汤及海鲜汤也值得一试。

STALL 铺 | #01-46 **PRICE** 价钱 | $ 4-6
OPENING HOURS 营业时间 | 09:00-14:00
Closed Wednesday & Saturday 周三及周六休息

HUAT HENG FRIED OYSTER
發興炒蚝煎

Fried baby oysters with eggs cooked-to-order.
即点即炒蚝仔煎。

STALL 铺 | #01-26　**PRICE** 价钱 | $ 5-8
OPENING HOURS 营业时间 | 13:00-21:00
Closed Monday　周一休息

Zion Riverside Food Centre
锡安河畔食阁

70 Zion Road 锡安路70号

Very popular in the district and, despite being located opposite a luxury shopping centre, it offers some good value food choices. The number of stalls may not be as extensive as other centres, but expect some renowned dishes like fried Kway Teow.

锡安河畔食阁为颇受本地人推荐的熟食中心，可能是因为虽然邻近高档购物中心世界城，但仍然提供价格相宜的用餐选择。中心内店铺相比其他地方略少，可是不论是小食的种类、味道或是知名度均绝不逊色。其中一家的炒粿条更是广为不同媒体所推荐，值得一试。

BOON TONG KEE KWAY CHAP · BRAISED DUCK
文通記

Braised duck and pork trotter are very popular. Order the braised duck rice set if you dine alone.

卤鸭和卤猪脚很受欢迎，单独用膳可点卤鸭饭套餐。

STALL 铺 | **#024 PRICE** 价钱 | $ 3-9
OPENING HOURS 营业时间 | 10:30-22:00

FRESH TASTE BIG PRAWN NOODLE
知味鮮大蝦面

The soup has a rich prawn flavour. Fresh prawns, chili and pork rinds combine to make a great bowl of noodles.

汤底虾味浓，虾鲜爽口，配以炸猪皮和辣椒，即叫即煮。

STALL 铺 | **#04 PRICE** 价钱 | $ 6-25
OPENING HOURS 营业时间 | 12:00-23:30

NO.18 ZION ROAD FRIED KWAY TEOW
NO.18炒粿條麵

Cooked-to-order. Robust flavours with a hint of spiciness; ingredients like fishcakes are a good match.

即叫即炒，味道浓而且香口，配有鱼片和蛳蚶，火候十足。

STALL 铺 | #017 **PRICE** 价钱 | $ 4-6
OPENING HOURS 营业时间 | 12:00-22:00

CENTRAL 中区

STREET FOOD
街头小吃

HILL STREET TAI HWA PORK NOODLE
大華豬肉粿條麵

Using fresh ingredients, the noodles are cooked-to-order and every bowl comes with its own instantly-made sauce and soup.

材料新鲜,每碗面均是独立烹煮,酱汁也是即时调和,常见人龙。

Blk 466, #01-12, Crawford Lane
哥罗福巷466座#01-12

PRICE 价钱 |
$ 5-10

OPENING HOURS 营业时间 |
09:30-21:00
Closed 1st and 3rd Monday of the month
每月第一及第三个周一休息

BISMILLAH BIRYANI

Biryani with fish or meat and flavoured with various Indian herbs.

以多种香料烹调的印度香饭像小山般堆在碟上,鱼和肉藏在其中,色香味美。

50 Dunlop Street
南洛街50号

PRICE 价钱 |
$ 6-20
OPENING HOURS 营业时间 |
11:30-15:00, 17:30-21:00

CENTRAL 中区

EMINENT FROG PORRIDGE & SEAFOOD (LOR 19)
明輝田雞粥海鮮煮炒店

It serves Cze Char dishes like Kung Pao frog, sweet and sour pork and fried crab with pepper.

各式煮炒小菜，如宫保田鸡、苦瓜鱼头、咕噜肉、黑椒蟹等。

Geylang Lorong 19, 323 Geylang Road
芽笼路323号芽笼里19巷

PRICE 价钱 |
$ 10-30
OPENING HOURS 营业时间 |
17:00-04:00

SIN KEE FAMOUS CANTONESE CHICKEN RICE
新記

Provides chicken rice with tender and juicy chicken. The homemade grated ginger and chili sauce is appetising. Dine-in only; come early as many dishes are gone by noon.

鸡肉嫩滑浓郁，米饭有嚼劲；自制姜蓉及辣椒汁更是开胃。不设外卖，且沽清便会关门，宜提早到访。

Block 40, Stall 7, #01-39, Holland Drive
荷兰通道40座#01-39 7号

PRICE 价钱 |
$ 4-30
OPENING HOURS 营业时间 |
11:00-16:00
Closed Monday 周一休息

🍴◯

JALAN SULTAN PRAWN MEE
惹蘭蘇丹蝦麵

A famous noodle stall with over 70 years of history; pork rib prawn mee is the most popular dish.

逾七十年历史的街头面档，经常满座，最有名的是汤底鲜甜的排骨虾面。

2 Jalan Ayer, Lorong 1 Geylang
芽笼1巷惹兰亚逸2号

PRICE 价钱 |
$ 5-10
OPENING HOURS 营业时间 |
08:00-15:30
Closed Tuesday　周二休息

🍴◯

LOR 9 BEEF KWAY TEOW
九巷牛河

Beef Kway Teow is their very popular signature dish. They also offer stir-fried dishes and seafood.

差不多每位客人都会点的牛肉炒河粉是此店的招牌菜，此外，还供应小炒菜式和海鲜。

237 Lorong 9 Geylang
芽笼9巷237号

PRICE 价钱 |
$ 6-30
OPENING HOURS 营业时间 |
11:00-03:00

CENTRAL 中区

HOTELS
酒店

Luxury · Elegant
豪华·典雅

MANDARIN ORIENTAL
文华东方

The Mandarin Oriental name is synonymous with luxury accommodation and impeccable service and this 'branch' of the international hotel group doesn't disappoint. Rising up from the fan-shaped courtyard are 21 floors of comfort and sophistication, with breathtaking views of Marina Bay. The colours, silks, linens and carvings all pay tribute to the hotel's unique setting.

欲享受新加坡的迷人气息，同时远离都市烦嚣，可考虑文华东方酒店。这幢有如酒店标志的扇子形建筑距离繁华的市中心只有数分钟路程，面朝滨海湾的醉人景致。大堂以云石和木制雕刻布置，气氛奢华优雅。无论服务、装潢或便利设施都无可挑剔。旅客更可到泳池、室外瑜伽亭和水疗中心尽情放松身心。

CENTRAL 中区

TEL. 6338 0066
www.mandarinoriental.com/singapore

Marina Square, 5 Raffles Avenue
莱佛士道5号滨海广场

468 **Rooms**/客房
59 **Suites**/套房

Price for 2 persons/双人房价格:
$ 349-1,025

Recommended restaurants/餐厅推荐:
Cherry Garden 櫻桃園
Dolce Vita

TEL. 6337 8888
www.ritzcarlton.com/singapore

7 Raffles Avenue
莱佛士道7号

529 **Rooms/**客房
79 **Suites/**套房

Price for 2 persons/双人房价格:
$ 1,188-1,540

Recommended restaurants/餐厅推荐:
Summer Pavilion 夏苑 ✿
Shiraishi 白石 🍴

Chain · Luxury
连锁式·豪华

THE RITZ-CARLTON, MILLENIA
丽思卡尔顿美年

It's not just the first-class services and facilities that set this hotel apart; it also comes with 4,200 pieces of artwork, including David Hockney, Zhu Wei and impressive Dale Chihuly glass sculptures. The public areas are designed according to the principles of feng shui and are exceptionally bright, thanks to the 10,000sqm of glass used in their construction.

踏进豪华精美的大堂,步伐自然会变慢,目光被四周充满视觉刺激的布置所吸引,弗兰克·斯特拉(Frank Stella)的雕塑和戴尔·奇胡利(Dale Chihuly)的玻璃艺术叫人凝神屏息,四千多件艺术品如星罗棋布。酒店占尽地利,景观耀眼,加上顶级的水疗服务……每个环节都天衣无缝,令人完全忘却外间的喧扰。

Luxury • Classic
豪华 • 经典

SHANGRI-LA
香格里拉

This resort-style hotel may be in the middle of the city but, thanks to the 15 acres of tropical garden that surround it, the atmosphere is peaceful and relaxing. If you want to make more of this tropical theme and feel closer to nature, ask for a bedroom in the Garden Wing – those in the Valley Wing are more classic in style but are also immaculately maintained.

酒店外十五英亩的青葱园林予人恬静平和之感，加上大堂内的大理石柱、螺旋形楼梯和落地窗，带来独一无二的豪华体验。房间分布于三个楼翼：塔翼典雅而富现代美感。设私人阳台的花园翼掩映于热带园林之中，还有室外按摩浴缸。峡谷翼从大堂、餐厅以至房间均私密度高，深得商务旅客欢心。

TEL. 6737 3644
www.shangri-la.com/singapore

22 Orange Grove
柑林路22号

743 **Rooms**/客房
49 **Suites**/套房

Price for 2 persons/双人房价格:
$ 360-870

Recommended restaurants/餐厅推荐:
Shang Palace 香宫 ⑪

CENTRAL 中区

199

TEL. 6734 1110
www.fourseasons.com/singapore

190 Orchard Boulevard
乌节林荫道190号

215 **Rooms**/客房
40 **Suites**/套房

Price for 2 persons/双人房价格:
$ 399-650

Recommended restaurants/餐厅推荐:
Jiang-Nan Chun 江南春 ❀

Luxury · Elegant
豪华 · 典雅

FOUR SEASONS
四季

There aren't many city hotels with tennis courts – the very exclusive Four Seasons hotel has four, two of which are indoor. It also has two swimming pools, one of which offers sweeping views of the city skyline. The newly renovated bedrooms are spacious and come equipped with every extra and amenity you'll ever need and the large marble bathrooms are particularly luxurious.

坐落于恬静优美、绿意盈盈的乌节林荫道,距离购物、娱乐和商业中心仅咫尺之遥。2017年修缮过的客房设计富现代气息,备有各式电子设施,云石浴室设备齐全。酒店设两个泳池,位于顶层的可饱览迷人天际线,另一个与水疗中心相连,感觉闲适写意。运动爱好者可尽情于健身室和网球场舒展。

Luxury · Elegant
豪华·典雅

INTERCONTINENTAL
洲际

It's not just its location in Bugis that makes this a worthy choice. A steady programme of improvement and refurbishment over the last few years has ensured its high standard of accommodation is maintained. The decoration cleverly blends Peranakan heritage with contemporary styles to create attractive and comfortable bedrooms – ask for one in the original building.

位于武吉士区的心脏地带，交通便利，再加上布置温馨的大堂、悦目的酒廊、舒适的客房及完善的餐饮设施，对旅客来说，确是极具吸引力。客房分布在十六层高、带有娘惹风情、设计时尚的主座大楼及充满殖民时代气息、娘惹风味更浓的小楼内，要时尚还是想怀旧？悉随尊便。

TEL. 6338 7600
www.intercontinental.com/
singapore

80 Middle Road
密驼路80号

370 **Rooms**/客房
33 **Suites**/套房
Price for 2 persons/双人房价格:
$ 290-700

Recommended restaurants/餐厅推荐:
Ash & Elm ⑪
Man Fu Yuan 满福苑 ⑪

CENTRAL 中区

♿ ⟨ 🛏 🅿 🍴 ♨ 🏊 🏋

TEL. 6333 8388
fullertonbayhotel.com

80 Collyer Quay
哥烈码头80号

94 **Rooms**/客房
6 **Suites**/套房

Price for 2 persons/双人房价格:
$ 485-1,240

Recommended restaurants/餐厅推荐:
The Clifford Pier ⒑

🏛

Luxury · Elegant
豪华·典雅

THE FULLERTON BAY
富丽敦海湾

Its angled glass façade ensures this waterfront hotel is instantly recognisable but what makes it really stand out is what's inside: four unique restaurants and a rooftop lounge, pool and garden – as well as bedrooms whose contemporary decorative elements manage to respect the past. And then there are the views: from every angle and in every direction.

坐落于滨海湾码头之上,倾斜的玻璃外墙异常耀眼夺目,滨海湾的景致叫人迷醉!时尚中带着殖民时代气息的装潢:柔和的灯光、丝绒沙发、几何图案、华丽的水晶吊灯……气派典雅高贵,还有体贴细心、令人愉悦的服务和完善的设施,难怪吸引不少文人雅士到此住宿。

CENTRAL 中区

Luxury • Elegant
豪华 • 典雅

THE ST. REGIS
瑞吉

Being within walking distance of both the Botanic Garden and Orchard Road means that this luxurious hotel ticks all the boxes as far as location is concerned, but it's the impressive art collection in the public areas that really sets it apart. Bedrooms come in chic designs, with bathrooms bedecked with French marble; ask for one facing the Botanic Garden.

金属玻璃外墙和豪华典雅的内部装潢，令酒店散发着奢华高雅的气派。四处陈列着顶级特色艺术品，包括国际知名艺术家的雕塑、绘画及版画，加上充满中国风情的布置，令客房格调雅致。房间备有一流的现代设施，部分可眺望植物园美景。水疗中心、桑拿浴室、蒸气房、健身室和室内网球场讓旅客盡享闲适的悠然时光。

TEL. 6506 6888
www.stregissingapore.com

29 Tanglin Road
东陵路29号

262 **Rooms**/客房
37 **Suites**/套房

Price for 2 persons/双人房价格:
$ 450-750

Recommended restaurants/餐厅推荐:
Shinji (Tanglin Road) ❄
Yan Ting 宴庭 🍴

CENTRAL 中区

♿ ⟨ 🛁 🅿 ⚕ 🏋 🎿 🆘 🧖

TEL. 6339 7777
www.fairmontsingapore.com

80 Bras Basah Road
勿拉士巴沙路80号

747 **Rooms**/客房
22 **Suites**/套房

Price for 2 persons/双人房价格:
$ 330-790

🏠🏠

Luxury · Luxury
豪华·豪华

FAIRMONT
费尔蒙

It may be located in Raffles City but The Fairmont offers nothing but tranquillity, whether you're by the pool, having a snack at Alligator Pear or sitting on a balcony overlooking the Marina. Ask for a room in the North Tower – not only has it been renovated, with a new look that pays homage to Singapore's past, but it also has the best views.

位于喧闹的莱佛士城内，面向迷人的滨海湾，这座充满娘惹风貌的酒店，却供给住客宁静的处所。不论是设备齐全的蔚柳溪水疗中心、或是宽敞舒适的客房，质素均在水准以上。悠闲的午后，到池畔餐厅品尝健康小食、享受水疗中心的专业服务或是在阳台上欣赏滨海湾景色，皆是赏心乐事。刚修葺过的北翼房间景观较佳。

Chain · Modern
连锁式·现代

GRAND HYATT
君悦

It may be geared largely towards the business community but, thanks to a terrific spa which boasts 11 treatment rooms as well as an impressive swimming pool, this international hotel is equally suited to those looking to spend their time at more leisurely pace. If you want a city atmosphere ask for the Grand Wing; if you want quiet, go for the Terrace Wing.

邻近乌节路和乌节地铁站的君悦酒店是商务和会议酒店,但亦适合休闲旅客入住。客房分布于Grand和Terrace楼翼,偏好宁静的不妨预订后者。客房面积宽广,设计时尚但不矫揉造作,便利设施应有尽有,个别更备独立起居室。泳池被绿茵树木环绕,静谧怡人。设有两个室外网球场。

TEL. 6738 1234
singapore.grand.hyatt.com

10 Scotts Road
史各士路10号

631 **Rooms/客房**
46 **Suites/套房**

Price for 2 persons/双人房价格:
$ 290-650

Recommended restaurants/餐厅推荐:
Mezza9 ⏺

CENTRAL 中区

205

CENTRAL 中区

& ≤ P ⚲ ♨ 🖼 🏊 💱 🧖

TEL. 6818 1888
jwmarriottsingapore.com

30 Beach Road
美芝路30号

587 **Rooms/**客房
47 **Suites/**套房

Price for 2 persons/双人房价格:
$ 380-550

Recommended restaurants/餐厅推荐:
Akira Back ⦿ **N**

Business • Art Deco
商务•艺术

JW MARRIOTT SOUTH BEACH **N**
万豪南岸

Unlike other hotels in this international chain, this one targets a younger business clientele, with art pieces dotting the hotel grounds. The Sky garden on the 6th floor provides both a swimming pool and unobstructed views of the Formula One racetrack. The hotel boasts 14 conference rooms, a number of food outlets, an executive lounge, a spa and an infinity pool on 18th floor.

酒店取年轻化定位,富艺术感的装饰设计别树一帜。具本地色彩的画作、雕塑等艺术品巧妙的散落于不同角落。酒店以照顾商务旅客为主,除了相应的房间设计,更设有十四间会议室及适合举办大型活动的场地。住客的休闲需要同样得到照顾,酒吧、贵宾酒廊及泳池齐备,更提供瑜伽、踢拳班等,甚至设特快按摩服务。

Resort • Contemporary
渡假村•时尚

MARINA BAY SANDS
滨海湾金沙

The three vast towers that make up this hotel, casino and conference centre are the city's most iconic structure. You'll need GPS to navigate through it, from the gambling tables to the vast array of shops and restaurants, to the pool and observation deck, but it'll be an exhilarating journey of discovery. Thanks to their floor-to-ceiling windows, bedrooms have unobstructed views.

坐落于滨海湾，三幢相连的宏伟时尚建筑，顶层是名闻遐迩的金沙空中花园及全球最大的无边际泳池，同楼层的观景台，让你将狮城景色尽收眼底。客房面积宽敞、环境舒适，且设备齐全，还能欣赏窗外的壮丽景色。酒店内的购物城有逾百家包含零售和餐饮服务的店铺，足不出酒店就能享受购物和大快朵颐之趣。

TEL. 6688 8868
www.marinabaysands.com

10 Bayfront Avenue
贝弗兰道10号

2,381 **Rooms**/客房
180 **Suites**/套房

Price for 2 persons/双人房价格:
$ 399-1,500

Recommended restaurants/餐厅推荐:
Waku Ghin ❀❀/ **Cut** ❀/
db Bistro & Oyster Bar ⚫/
Long Chim ⚫/ **Spago** ⚫

TEL. 6809 8888
www.parkroyalhotels.com/
pickering

3 Upper Pickering Street
皮克林街上段3号

338 **Rooms**/客房
29 **Suites**/套房

Price for 2 persons/双人房价格:
$ 290-460

Business · Luxury
商务 · 豪华

PARKROYAL ON PICKERING
皮克林宾乐雅

One of the more original looking hotels in Singapore is made up of three glass towers linked by Sky Gardens. Its eco-credentials are very much in evidence throughout, with its use of natural materials and living walls of plants. All the stylish bedrooms have views of the city skyline. If you don't suffer from vertigo ask for a room on one of the Sky Garden floors.

装潢以木、石、水和植物等大自然元素作主题，更显环保意念。设计现代兼具个性的客房能观赏一望无尽的天际；水疗中心内的无边际泳池，景色更是扣人心弦。建议选择空中花园楼层的房间，闲来在房外的小径散步解郁，煞是美好。街面楼层的Lime环境舒适，供应多国美食，疲惫懒动时也是不错的进餐选择。

Luxury • Traditional
豪华 • 传统

REGENT
丽晶

The impressive atrium lobby sets the tone and this sense of comfort and elegance is continued in the bedrooms, which blend Asian and Western styles. The location is also good as the hotel is within walking distance of the Botanic Gardens and the shops of Orchard Road. Another striking feature is the Manhattan bar – a very glamorous space inspired by old New York.

酒店位处优越地段，步行即可抵达植物园或乌节路，会议设施齐备。客房融合中西设计精髓，典雅中不失便利，套房更享私人露台。想尽情放松，可以到漩涡浴池、按摩浴池、蒸气浴室或桑拿房。嗜杯中物者不妨到访Manhattan酒吧，置身怀旧情调的酒吧中，细品匠心调制的香醇美酒，实是人生乐事。

TEL. 6733 8888
www.regenthotels.com/regent-singapore

1 Cuscaden Road
卡斯加登路1号

394 **Rooms**/客房
46 **Suites**/套房

Price for 2 persons/双人房价格:
$ 260-360

Recommended restaurants/餐厅推荐:
Summer Palace 夏宫 ❀

CENTRAL 中区

TEL. 6733 8388
www.fullertonhotels.com

1 Fullerton Square
浮尔顿广场1号

372 **Rooms**/客房
28 **Suites**/套房

Price for 2 persons/双人房价格:
$ 278-718

Recommended restaurants/餐厅推荐:
Jade 玉楼 🍴◐
The Lighthouse 🍴◐

Historic building • Traditional
历史建筑•传统

THE FULLERTON
富丽敦

From General Post Office to National Monument, the story of the huge, forever busy neo-classical Fullerton is one that's inexorably linked to the emergence of Singapore as a modern city of the world. The interior may not quite match the splendour of the building itself but the bedrooms come with thoughtful little touches and all have either city or water views.

这幢富历史意义的古典时尚建筑物获政府列为国家古迹之一。宽敞的客房设计清雅,窗外景色更是幽雅迷人。房间的设备很完善,能体贴客人的需要,例如衣橱内设有一个神秘柜子供住客摆放鞋子,特别的是住客把鞋子放进柜内,隔天再拿出来时会发现鞋子给擦得光光亮亮。

Historic building · Design
历史建筑 · 型格

SOFITEL SO SINGAPORE
索菲特

This iconic building, built in 1927 and formerly home to Singapore Telecommunications, now hosts this very stylish boutique hotel – some of its striking design elements are courtesy of Karl Lagerfeld. Room categories begin with the very compact 'So Cosy'; try a 'So Urban', 'So Vip', 'So Lofty' or 'So Studio'. 'Hi So' is the rooftop pool and trendy bar.

建筑物建于1927年，是新加坡电讯公司的旧址，为狮城地标，现已变成这间设计时尚别致、带有强烈个人风格的精品酒店。分布于两翼的房间，保留了建筑物原有风味再配以时尚的家俬摆设，非常雅致。住客可到第七层的天台泳池和酒吧舒展身心。位于大堂的咖啡店供应经典及渗入了亚洲风味的法国菜。

TEL. 6701 6800
www.sofitel-so-singapore.com

35 Robinson Road
罗敏申路35号

123 **Rooms**/客房
16 **Suites**/套房

Price for 2 persons/双人房价格:
$ 300-800

CENTRAL 中区

211

TEL. 6338 8333
www.carltonhotel.sg
76 Bras Basah Road
勿拉士峇沙路76号

932 **Rooms**/客房
8 **Suites**/套房
Price for 2 persons/双人房价格:
$ 260-720

Recommended restaurants/餐厅推荐:
Shinji (Bras Basah Road) ❀
Wah Lok 華樂 🍴

Business · Contemporary
商务·时尚

CARLTON
卡尔登

Business travellers will find the location ideal, especially as it is just a few minutes' walk to convention venues and three main MRT stations, along with large shopping centres and various restaurants. This is the largest independently-owned hotel in Singapore, with 930 bedrooms – these are bright, spacious and sufficiently well-equipped.

设有逾九百个房间的卡尔登酒店是新加坡最大的独立酒店,设施及服务均符合国际标准。其选址占尽地利,离会议展览场所及三条主要地铁线道仅数分钟步行距离,是商务停留的一流之选,附近亦有大型购物中心和众多食肆。房间光亮,空间充裕,室内设计时尚实用且设施齐全,床单的素质亦好。

Business • Contemporary
商务 • 时尚

CARLTON CITY
卡尔登城市

This sister hotel to The Carlton in Civic is on the edge of the CBD and offers up to date facilities for business travellers. Bedrooms are bright and modern and offer either Chinatown or harbour views. There are also good views from the Graffiti bar on the 29th floor. 'Plate' serves international dishes and overlooks the pool and sun terrace.

卡尔登城市坐落于中央商业区一角,靠近丹戎巴葛地铁站,不论是公干或旅游,其地点都很便利。酒店的建筑和设计风格时尚独特,从客房能俯瞰醉人的港湾或繁华的牛车水景色。欲饱览狮城海岸美景可到位于29层的酒吧喝一杯。行政楼层客房及设施是商务人士理想之选。

TEL. 6632 8888
www.carltoncity.sg

1 Gopeng Street
高平街1号

384 **Rooms**/客房
2 **Suites**/套房

Price for 2 persons/双人房价格:
$ 450

CENTRAL 中区

CENTRAL 中区

TEL. 6334 8888
www.conradsingapore.com

2 Temasek Boulevard
淡马锡林荫道2号

487 **Rooms/**客房
25 **Suites/**套房

Price for 2 persons/双人房价格:
$ 270-790

Recommended restaurants/餐厅推荐:
Golden Peony 金牡丹

Business • Traditional
商务•传统

CONRAD CENTENNIAL
康莱德

There's no doubt this hotel will satisfy anyone who is looking for a well run and comfortable hotel in a good location – one that offers large bedrooms, a good cocktail bar and a relaxing lounge. What really sets this place apart however, is the vast and impressive collection of paintings and sculptures that are scattered around the building.

得天独厚的地理位置、宽敞舒适的住宿环境和宾至如归的服务，都令旅客对这酒店趋之若鹜，俯拾皆是的博物馆级艺术藏品，更为旅客带来美妙的住宿体验。开阔的大堂吧富丽堂皇，是享用鸡尾酒和现场音乐的绝佳场所。中餐厅金牡丹提供的美食定能令旅客饱腹而归。

Historic building · Modern
历史建筑·现代

FORT CANNING
福康宁

The city may be on the doorstep but it'll feel miles away when you're on the shady patio of this rather grand building, which was built in 1926 for the British army – little wonder it's a popular wedding venue too. A more contemporary building houses the bedrooms; ask for a bathroom with natural light. The Tisettanta Lounge is the place for a good cocktail.

建于1926年，原为英军行政大楼。虽位处市中心，然而隐藏在绿树成荫的公园内，予人宁谧之感。前排客房面向繁华市中心，后排客房是清幽园景。房间设计富现代感，与古雅的酒店建筑相映成趣。幽雅的花园景色、清澈的泉水泳池加上完备的场地设施，是举办婚宴的热门场地。

TEL. 6559 6770
www.hfcsingapore.com
11 Canning Walk
康宁径11号

79 **Rooms**/客房
7 **Suites**/套房
Price for 2 persons/双人房价格:
$ 268-550

CENTRAL 中区

Historic building • Functional
历史建筑 • 实用

GOODWOOD PARK
良木园

No roll-call of Singapore hotels would be complete without Goodwood Park. Built in 1900 as the Teutonia Club for German expats, it became a hotel in the late 1920s and has been enlarged and improved over time, culminating in its Grand Tower becoming a National Monument in 1989. Bedrooms are soberly decorated, with the 'Heritage Rooms' being the most elegant.

建于1900年的良木园是本地历史最悠久的酒店之一，其塔楼于1989年获列为国立纪念物，原是侨居当地德国商界名流聚集的条顿俱乐部(Teutonia Club)，于30年代修缮成酒店。坐落市中心，四周是翠绿葱葱的园林，房间设计素雅而设施齐备，豪华塔楼客房设计富殖民地风格，为旅客提供远离烦嚣的休闲空间。

TEL. 6737 7411
www.goodwoodparkhotel.com

22 Scotts Road
史各士路22号

212 **Rooms**/客房
21 **Suites**/套房

Price for 2 persons/双人房价格:
$ 320-1,200

Recommended restaurants/餐厅推荐:
Alma ✿
Gordon Grill ⑩
Min Jiang 岷江川菜馆 ⑩

THE SMARTER WAY TO DINE.

Use promo code **MGS18** to earn 400 Chope-Dollars for your first reservation; exchangeable for a $10 dining voucher.

DISCOVER RESTAURANTS | **BOOK** TABLES | **SAVE** WITH DEALS

Luxury • Contemporary
豪华 • 时尚

MANDARIN ORCHARD
文华

The spacious bedrooms look more contemporary, thanks to the refurbishment in 2017. The hotel dates from 1971 and enjoys a good location on Orchard Road, with shopping centres and MRT stations on its doorstep. The rooms have good views but nothing matches the 360° vistas from the Meritus Club Lounge on the top floor.

这家于1971年已营业的酒店坐落在繁忙的乌节路上，邻近各大购物商场，离两个地铁站也只是数分钟步行距离，非常方便。刚於2017年完成翻新工程的客房已换上更时尚的装饰，景观开扬，空间充裕。位于M楼座顶层环状的Meritus Club Lounge更可俯瞰全市美景。

TEL. 6737 4411
www.meritushotels.com
/mandarin-orchard-singapore

333 Orchard Road
乌节路333号

1,048 **Rooms**/客房
29 **Suites**/套房

Price for 2 persons/双人房价格:
$ 300-700

Recommended restaurants/餐厅推荐:
Shisen Hanten 四川飯店 ✷✷

CENTRAL 中区

TEL. 6363 0101
www.onefarrer.com

1 Farrer Park Station Road
花拉公园站路1号

224 Rooms/客房
19 Suites/套房

Price for 2 persons/双人房价格:
$ 250-430

Business • Contemporary
商务•时尚

ONE FARRER
华乐

Some may consider this self-styled 'urban resort' hotel, which opened in 2014, a little too far from the city centre but Farrer Park MRT station is directly underneath the 20 storey building. The large spa and 50m swimming pool certainly add to its appeal, as do the many pieces of artwork. Longer staying guests should consider the Loft Apartments or Sky Villas.

酒店楼高二十层，位于花拉公园地铁站之上，邻近有许多景点名胜，地点非常便利。现代设计加上时尚摆设的客房充满城市感觉，偌大的玻璃窗外是热闹且具有浓厚地方色彩的小印度街景，感觉蛮舒适。第六层的奥运标准泳池、设备完善的健身中心及水疗设施，是一天繁忙后或空闲时最佳的消闲处。

Business • Functional
商务•实用

ORCHARD
乌节

Bedrooms in this large yet conveniently located hotel are divided between two wings: The Orchard Wing, opened in 1985, has the more functional rooms; those in the newer Claymore Wing are far better as they were refurbished more recently and are larger and quieter. This is the wing that also hosts the chic Signature rooms created by the interior designer Pierre Yves Rochon.

从酒店步行至静谧的新加坡植物园或繁华的乌节娱乐购物地段都十分方便。房间分布于两幢楼翼,建议预订翻新过的Claymore楼翼,其设计时尚,房间面积较宽广,环境宁静舒适。其中贵宾行政客房由著名室内设计师Pierre Yves Rochon精心设计,融合东方和欧洲元素,时尚豪华。

TEL. 6734 7766
www.orchardhotel.com.sg
442 Orchard Road
乌节路442号

636 **Rooms**/客房
20 **Suites**/套房

Price for 2 persons/双人房价格:
$ 220-600

Recommended restaurants/餐厅推荐:
Hua Ting 華廳 ⑪○

CENTRAL 中区

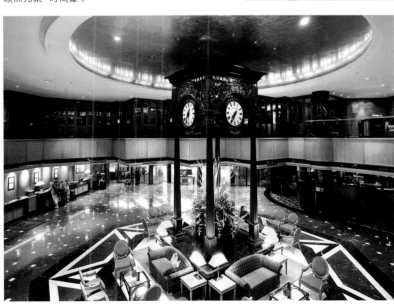

TEL. 6336 8111
www.panpacific.com/singapore

7 Raffles Boulevard
莱佛士林荫道7号

746 **Rooms**/客房
44 **Suites**/套房

Price for 2 persons/双人房价格:
$ 280-1,050

Recommended restaurants/餐厅推荐:
Rang Mahal

Chain · Elegant
连锁式·典雅

PAN PACIFIC
泛太平洋

Immaculate upkeep ensures that this not-so-new kid on the block still gleams. It's a good option for business travellers and those on longer stays as its location is excellent – it's linked to Marina Square and Millenia Walk and all the boutiques and food courts you'll ever need. It also has two high-end restaurants of its own, along with a never-ending buffet.

客房空间感十足、整洁明亮、设施便利,是商务旅客或长期旅客的绝佳之选。酒店邻近购物热点滨海广场及美年径,满足购物和享用美食的欲望。若不想走得太远,酒店内也有不同餐厅任君选择,不论是印度菜馆Rang Mahal、中餐厅,或提供早、午自助餐的自助餐室,都能大快朵颐。

Chain · Classic
连锁式·经典

SHERATON TOWERS
喜来登

Opened in the mid '80s, this business hotel is usefully located and its bedrooms, which come with floor-to-ceiling windows, are fully equipped with all the necessary extras demanded by the modern business traveler. The Pool & Terrace rooms on the 5th floor come with private balconies which look onto the very pleasant swimming pool and garden.

这间于1985年开业的商务酒店予人温暖舒适之感。房间设计典雅，大玻璃窗外是繁华的史各士路，配有便利齐全的现代化设施，满足商务旅客需要。五楼的露台客房和泳池客房设有独立阳台，可将泳池景致尽收眼底。想让身体尽情流汗？可到同一层的健身中心或桑拿浴室去，绝对能让你整天精力充沛。

TEL. 6737 6888
www.sheratonsingapore.com

39 Scotts Road
史各士路39号

402 **Rooms**/客房
18 **Suites**/套房

Price for 2 persons/双人房价格:
$ 320-840

CENTRAL 中区

Chain · Luxury
连锁式·豪华

SWISSÔTEL THE STAMFORD
史丹福瑞士

What was once the world's tallest hotel can still boast of having some of the city's largest bedrooms. It is also the hotel of choice for many fans of Formula 1 due to its coveted position on the circuit – there's even a heliport for ticket holders who are financially more fortunate. Service levels have always been high and there's a host of bars, cafés and restaurants.

全赖良好的定期维修，虽已开业三十年，感觉仍然簇新。客房宽敞舒适，窗外景致尤为动人。要欣赏最迷人景色，切记要求入住面向海景的房间，不光能欣赏幽美的落日景致，还能观看酒店举行的各样活动如新年烟花、音乐会。酒店位于滨海湾跑道第九个弯处，欲观赏本年F1方程式大赛晚间赛事，这儿是不错的选择。

TEL. 6338 8585
www.swissotel.com/singapore-stamford

2 Stamford Road
史丹福路2号

1,232 **Rooms**/客房
29 **Suites**/套房

Price for 2 persons/双人房价格:
$ 350-450

Recommended restaurants/餐厅推荐:
Jaan ❀

Chain · Traditional
连锁式·传统

THE WESTIN
威斯汀

Smack in the middle of what locals refer to as 'the new frontier' sits this bright, modern hotel for global financial types. The neatly decorated bedrooms are on floors 36-46 so there's little noise to disturb a night's sleep, once all surrounding cranes are quietened. If you're a keen jogger new to the city you can engage the services of the Running Concierge.

酒店坐落于新金融商业区心脏地带,客房位于36-46层,高耸的位置能隔绝地面噪音。房间宽敞、睡床舒适,能让你酣畅入睡。有运动习惯的旅客可轻装入住,酒店提供运动装备租借服务,更可跟随酒店的跑步礼宾师一同路跑,尽情呼吸户外空气,重唤活力。酒店邻近地铁站,交通便捷。

TEL. 6922 6888
www.thewestinsingapore.com

Asia Square Tower 2,
12 Marina View
滨海景12号亚洲广场2号塔

289 **Rooms**/客房
16 **Suites**/套房

Price for 2 persons/双人房价格:
$ 350-1,200

CENTRAL 中区

Boutique hotel · Design
精品酒店·型格

NAUMI

There are a number of good reasons to choose this boutique hotel: its interesting architectural features and great location just behind Raffles hotel, its appealingly arty atmosphere, and the seductive décor and attention to detail of its bedrooms. If you want a larger room ask for one of the 'designer rooms' inspired by Andy Warhol or Coco Chanel.

有趣的建筑风格、艺术气息浓厚的大堂，会否令你驻足于此？设计时尚的客房精致小巧，配合优质床具，感觉蛮舒服。私隐度高的天台泳池和附属的露天酒廊，是繁忙过后舒缓紧张情绪的最佳选择。欲选择面积较宽敞的客房，可以考虑灵感源自两位不同领域的设计大师——安迪沃荷、可可香奈儿——的设计师客房。

TEL. 6403 6000
www.naumihotels.com

41 Seah Street
余街41号

73 **Rooms/客房**

Price for 2 persons/双人房价格:
$ 340-420

Business • Design
商务 • 型格

OASIA DOWNTOWN
中豪亚

No one can miss this distinctive tower of red metal entwined with a vertical garden. The hotel opened in 2016 and its lobby is an amazing open space with great city views. Warm, understated bedrooms all have floor-to-ceiling windows and an elegant Scandinavian feel. There are two pools on the rooftop and an all-day dining space on the 1st floor.

这幢楼高27层的酒店2016年开始营业,红色金属外墙加上缭绕四周的植物,营造了别树一帜的外貌。大堂位处开放的十二层,可俯瞰城市美景。西班牙籍设计师为房间挑选了色调温暖而设计典雅的木镶板,配以简洁的家具摆设,为商务和休闲旅客提供了宁静舒适的休息场所。顶层的两个泳池是舒展身心的好去处。

TEL. 6812 6900
www.oasiahotels.com/en/
singapore

100 Peck Seah Street
柏城街100号

312 **Rooms**/客房
2 **Suites**/套房
Price for 2 persons/双人房价格:
$ 260-290

CENTRAL 中区

CENTRAL 中区

♿ 🅿 🛏 🖼 🛋

TEL. 6291 6677
www.hotelvagabondsingapore.com

39 Syed Alwi Road
赛阿威路39号

36 **Rooms**/客房
5 **Suites**/套房

Price for 2 persons/双人房价格:
$ 200-500

🏠

Boutique hotel • Cosy
精品酒店•舒适

VAGABOND

When a hotel has its own artist in residence you know it's going to be a little different. This 1950s building has been transformed into a theatrically decorated and charming boutique hotel; it is full of original touches and comes with an atmosphere all of its own. The bedrooms may be somewhat compact but great care has gone into their decoration.

地点不在商业区,亦非便利,却位处小印度和十榜格南中间,令这家建于1950年、装潢时髦舒适的精品酒店多了点韵味。店主和设计师千挑万选出逾百幅油画、相片及原创作品:接待台前的犀牛和大堂的大象雕塑等装饰令整间酒店生色不少。客房较密集和细小,但木制家具和温暖的布置却令人有家的感觉。

Business • Modern
商务·现代

JEN ORCHARDGATEWAY
乌节门今旅

Opened in 2014 in the heart of Orchard Road, this hotel is directly connected to three different shopping malls as well as Somerset MRT station. There's cutting-edge technology throughout the hotel and bedrooms are bright, modern and functional. As their name suggests, the Panorama Club rooms have the best views. There are also three terrific rooftop pools.

酒店耸立于乌节路心脏地带，2014年开业，邻近索美塞地铁站和三个购物商场，占尽地利。酒店配备最尖端的设备，房间视野开阔，高级和豪华客房分别适合短期和长期旅客。欲饱览天际景致，不能错过顶级全景贵宾廊客房。酒店顶层设有三个别具一格的游泳池，让你静赏城市全景，更可享受按摩服务。

TEL. 6708 8888
www.hoteljen.com/
orchardgateway

Level 10, 277 Orchard Road
乌节路277号10层

499 **Rooms**/客房

Price for 2 persons/双人房价格:
$ 250-420

CENTRAL 中区

227

CENTRAL 中区

TEL. 6580 2888
www.stayfareast.com/amoy
76 Telok Ayer Street
直落亚逸街76号

37 **Rooms**/客房

Price for 2 persons/双人房价格:
$ 298-378

🏠

Boutique hotel · Design
精品酒店·型格

AMOY
华绣

Part boutique hotel, part museum, the very individual Amoy hotel is set around the former Fuk Tak Chi temple which is now home to an exhibition about Singapore's Chinese immigrants. Blending traditional architecture with new designs, the 'cosy singles' and 'deluxe doubles' spread around this historic building make good use of natural materials. Complimentary Limousine service to the airport is included if you are booking directly to the hotel.

位处福德祠遗址，一半是精品酒店，一半是仍然保留了祠堂原貌、介绍本地华裔移民历史的博物馆，蛮有趣的一间酒店！大堂内还保留着寺庙原来的水井，不论是馨逸单人房还是豪华双人房，每间房间最少有一件古代工艺品作装饰，风格全是古旧中隐隐透着时代感。免费的机场接送服务还附有博物馆导览服务。

Business · Functional
商务 · 实用

BENCOOLEN
明古连

A simple hotel, not without a certain style, that's ideal for a short stay. Bedrooms come in a variety of categories – the 'Executive' rooms provide a little more space. Breakfast is help-yourself from the buffet in an area that doubles as the lounge and reception. For those staying a little longer there's a pantry in which to prepare meals and do washing.

从1968年便开始经营酒店业务的明古连家族旗下的年轻成员。面积不大、设计简约却是五脏俱全，适合短期住宿的旅客。房间类型从普通的阁楼客房至奢华高尚的豪华房，切合不同客人需求。第六层是屋顶阳台，其上附有按摩功能的小泳池。喜欢下厨的住客可自购食材在酒店的茶水间亲手炮制最爱餐点。

TEL. 6460 4933
www.hotelbencoolen.com
47 Hong Kong Street
香港街47号

28 **Rooms**/客房
4 **Suites**/套房
Price for 2 persons/双人房价格:
$ 200-300

CENTRAL 中区

CENTRAL 中区

TEL. 6396 3322
www.wanderlusthotel.com

2 Dickson Road
狄生路2号

20 **Rooms**/客房
9 **Suites**/套房

Price for 2 persons/双人房价格:
$ 210-400

Historic building · Trendy
历史建筑 · 前卫

WANDERLUST

A converted school from the 1920s in lively Little India is the setting for this charming and vibrant hotel with a look all of its own. What the bedrooms lack in space they more than make up for in their decoration; each floor has its own theme and each room is different. The ersatz-industrial looking restaurant has communal tables and a French menu.

这家与热闹的小印度相邻，Unlisted Collection集团麾下的酒店装潢时尚且别树一帜。客房面积较小，设计和布置倒是充满生气。以单色或鲜艳的色系如黄、红、紫、青等将客房区分，每个色系均有自己的歌曲，例如U2的Red Light；披头四的Yellow Submarine。想空间多点，可考虑Momo或Whimsical系列的客房。

Th. Haupt/Westend61 RM / Photononstop

SOUTH WEST
西南

RESTAURANTS
餐厅

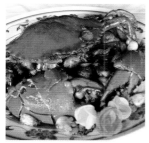

NEW UBIN SEAFOOD
(BUKIT BATOK)

Singaporean • Simple
新加坡菜•简朴

Look for the sign saying 'canteen' or you'll never find this Cze Char kitchen. It's a simple spot, albeit slightly bigger than its last premises – the photos on the wall record the development of the restaurant over the years. The butter crab is well worth ordering but don't ignore the charcoal-grilled American rib-eye. At lunch the space is shared with two other food stalls so it might be better to come for dinner.

店外只悬着一个印上"Canteen"的招牌，很难察觉里面便是这家餐馆。迁址后的餐馆，面积更大、更宽敞，装修风格却与旧址无甚分别，墙上排列有序的旧照片诉说着餐馆过去与现在的故事。包罗万有的餐单，除了提供地道的海鲜和煮炒菜式，还包括必点菜炭烤美国肉眼扒。

P ⇄ 65 ☏🍽

TEL. 6466 9558

Lam Soon Industrial Building, Level 6, 63 Hillview Avenue
山景道63号南顺工业大厦6层
www.ubinseafood.com

■ **PRICE 价钱**
Lunch 午膳
à la carte 点菜 $ 10-30
Dinner 晚膳
à la carte 点菜 $ 40-80

■ **OPENING HOURS 营业时间**
Lunch 午膳 11:30-14:30 (L.O.)
Dinner 晚膳 17:30-21:45 (L.O.)

■ **ANNUAL AND WEEKLY CLOSING**
休息日期
Closed 2 days Lunar New Year and Monday lunch
农历新年2天及周一午膳休息

SOUTH WEST 西南

SOUTH WEST 西南

♿ ♨ 🅿 💺12 🍴 ⛲

TEL. 6577 6599

**Crockfords Tower, G2,
Resorts World Sentosa,
8 Sentosa Gateway**

圣淘沙桥门8号圣淘沙名胜世界
康乐福豪华酒店G2
www.rwsentosa.com/dining

■ **PRICE 价钱**
Lunch 午膳
set 套餐 $ 50-100
à la carte 点菜 $ 50-130
Dinner 晚膳
set 套餐 $ 100-500
à la carte 点菜 $ 50-130

■ **OPENING HOURS 营业时间**
Lunch 午膳 11:00-15:00 (L.O.)
Dinner 晚膳 18:00-23:00 (L.O.)
Friday, Saturday & Public Holidays
eve dinner 周五、六及公众假期前夕
晚膳 18:00-01:00 (L.O.)

🍴○

FENG SHUI INN
风水廷

Cantonese • Elegant
粤菜 • 典雅

It may be hidden away on the ground floor of
Crockfords Tower but this Cantonese restaurant
is well worth seeking out. The large dining room is
elegantly decorated with superb lacquered panels
and granite walls. The signature dishes include
highly nutritious double-boiled soups, Canadian
geoduck clams, crispy fish skin, and pan-fried tiger
prawns. At lunch, don't miss the baked yam pastry
or the steamed prawn dumplings on the list of dim
sum.

由在香港从事厨师多年的经验老师傅掌厨，以极新鲜
食材炮制的粤菜味道令人垂涎。青柠黄金脆鱼皮、豉
油皇干煎老虎虾、古法牛柳粒等均为其拿手菜。说到粤
菜，当然少不了老火汤，天天新款的风水廷老火汤是必
试之选。午市点心的风水鲜虾饺和香芋黄金角同样不
能错过。

FOREST
森

Asian contemporary • Design
时尚亚洲菜 • 型格

To best experience the modern, innovative dishes of celebrity chef Sam Leong, come here to the Equarius hotel for dinner rather than lunch. Signature dishes include milky chicken broth with morel mushrooms and bamboo; Sichuan-style mapo tofu with crab meat; and beef tenderloin with foie gras and black pepper sauce. Service in this airy, high-ceilinged dining room with its forest motif is courteous and eager. Sunday lunch offers a set menu only.

淡棕色树叶绘图，落地玻璃窗和门，花园景致一览无遗。大厨以新颖的烹调手法处理来自亚洲各地的食材，透过反传统的烹饪概念替中国菜进行革新。午餐菜单较简单，欲品尝美味中菜，要于晚饭时间到访。野生竹笙羊肚菌牛奶鸡汤、川式麻婆豆腐蟹肉蒸饭及黑椒牛柳粒伴鹅肝是招牌菜。周日午市只供应套餐。

TEL. 6577 7788

**Equarius Hotel, Lobby,
Resorts World Sentosa,
8 Sentosa Gateway**

圣淘沙桥门8号圣淘沙名胜世界
逸濠酒店大堂楼层

www.rwsentosa.com/dining

■ **PRICE 价钱**
Lunch 午膳
set 套餐 $ 42-138
à la carte 点菜 $ 50-220
Dinner 晚膳
set 套餐 $ 138-268
à la carte 点菜 $ 50-220

■ **OPENING HOURS 营业时间**
Lunch 午膳 12:00-14:15 (L.O.)
Sunday lunch 周日午膳
12:00-14:30 (L.O.)
Dinner 晚膳 18:00-22:15 (L.O.)

SOUTH WEST 西南

♿ 🏮 🍵 🅿 ⇔50 ⊙🍴

TEL. 6774 0122

5 Rochester Park
罗彻斯德园5号
www.goodwoodparkhotel.com

■ **PRICE 价钱**
Lunch 午膳
set 套餐 $ 58-98
à la carte 点菜 $ 30-180
Dinner 晚膳
set 套餐 $ 58-98
à la carte 点菜 $ 30-180

■ **OPENING HOURS 营业时间**
Lunch 午膳 11:30-14:00 (L.O.)
Dinner 晚膳 18:30-22:00 (L.O.)

🍴

MIN JIANG AT ONE-NORTH
岷江在纬壹

Chinese · Historic
中国菜·古典

The Beijing duck roasted in a wood-fired oven has gained almost legendary status at this Chinese restaurant which occupies a charming, colonial style house in a small park. Other specialities include stewed lobster with eggplant; pan-fried scallops with crab meat; and braised Wagyu beef cheeks with papaya. Sit on the decked terrace surrounded by plants and trees and you'll really appreciate what a tranquil spot this is.

由良木园酒店经营,布置带有殖民时期色彩,精致的餐室,四周满布植物与树丛、环境宁静,是闹市中的一股清泉。餐单方面,多款川粤菜可供挑选,经典菜式如古法木材烤北京鸭也有供应。招牌菜还包括茄子龙虾、厨师前菜拼盘、蟹肉煎带子等。

OSIA
澳西亚

Australian contemporary •
Contemporary
时尚澳洲菜 • 时尚

"Every dish has a story to tell" is how the young chef, under the direction of Scott Webster, describes his cuisine. The creative dishes use prime produce from Australia and Asia and the chefs in their open kitchen take centre stage in the light, modern dining room. Start with ceviche before moving on to main courses like sea perch with soy milk curd, grilled Grainge Black Angus beef, or Byron Bay Berkshire pork chops cooked in the stone hearth oven.

顾名思义，餐厅名字已然道出了其供应的是澳洲菜式，新颖的配搭和严谨的用料选材，组合成新派的料理，令人眼前一亮。餐酒单提供约二百款包含新、旧世界品种的葡萄酒，于圣淘沙玩乐后与三五知己浅酌确是赏心乐事。

TEL. 6577 6560
Resorts World Sentosa,
#02-140/141, 26 Sentosa Gateway

圣淘沙桥门26号
圣淘沙名胜世界#02-140/141
www.rwsentosa.com/dining

■ **PRICE 价钱**
Lunch 午膳
set 套餐 $ 39-49
à la carte 点菜 $ 80-350
Dinner 晚膳
set 套餐 $ 110-150
à la carte 点菜 $ 80-350

■ **OPENING HOURS 营业时间**
Lunch 午膳 12:00-14:15 (L.O.)
Dinner 晚膳 18:00-22:00 (L.O.)

■ **ANNUAL AND WEEKLY CLOSING**
休息日期
Closed Wednesday 周三休息

SOUTH WEST 西南

🄿 ⇔60 ⃝

TEL. 6276 9138

**Keppel Club, M level,
10 Bukit Chermin Road**
武吉慈明路10号岜巴俱乐部M层
www.peonyjade.com

■ **PRICE** 价钱
Lunch 午膳
set 套餐 $ 42-45
à la carte 点菜 $ 50-100
Dinner 晚膳
set 套餐 $ 38
à la carte 点菜 $ 50-100

■ **OPENING HOURS** 营业时间
Lunch 午膳 11:00-14:30 (L.O.)
Dinner 晚膳 18:00-22:30 (L.O.)
Sunday dinner 周日晚膳
18:00-23:00 (L.O.)

■ **ANNUAL AND WEEKLY CLOSING**
休息日期
Closed 1 day in the month of Lunar
New Year 农历正月休息1天

🍴○

PEONY JADE (KEPPEL)
玉河畔 (吉宝)

Cantonese • Oriental décor
粤菜•东方

You don't need to be a member of Keppel Club to visit its Cantonese restaurant. In a large room with beams, dark wood panelling and hanging red lanterns, you'll find food that's full of flavour, carefully prepared and reasonably priced. On the dim sum lunch menu, the hot and sour meat dumplings and pan-fried radish cake with preserved meat are a must. On the main menu try the deep-fried prawns with creamy egg yolk along with some Sichuan dishes.

香软奶皇流沙包、京川饺子、腊味煎萝卜糕、鲜虾腐皮卷、脆皮明虾角、京都排骨……全是光听名字便会令你口角垂涎的经典粤式美食，也是主厨的看家菜。木梁天花、红红的灯笼、绘有国画的中式屏风和红木中式家具摆设，带有浓浓中国风的设计，让你不论在味觉还是视觉上都能饱尝传统的味道。

NESPRESSO
PROFESSIONAL

A PINCH OF EXCELLENCE

Served by more than 750 top-rated chefs.

Discover **Nespresso** Professional coffee solutions
on **nespresso.com/pro** or call 800 186 5007

what else?

SYUN
春

Japanese contemporary •
Exotic décor
时尚日本菜•异国风情

One should never judge restaurants by their façades but it's hard not to have one's expectations raised by the sight of the sweet little garden at the entrance to this discreet and warmly run Japanese restaurant. The contemporary cuisine comes with lots of modern twists, with dishes like sea urchin rolled in Wagyu beef, and grilled cod with yuzu miso sauce and dried millet powder. Equal thought has gone into the sake list.

进入由黑白石头组成的仿日本花园入口后，是这家布置柔和温暖的日本食店。两位经验丰富的日本师傅合力制作的菜式，充满创造力且揉合了时尚风与传统风味，选用的材料亦非常新鲜。和牛海胆卷、西京味噌鳕鱼和寿司盖饭是这儿的名菜。清酒单还包含了厨师推介的生酛酒系列，颇为特别。

☃ 🅿 ⇔8 🚗 ◐🍽

TEL. 6577 6867

Resorts World Sentosa,
#02-135/135A, 8 Sentosa Gateway

圣淘沙桥门8号
圣淘沙名胜世界#02-135/135A
www.rwsentosa.com/dining

■ **PRICE 价钱**
Lunch 午膳
set 套餐 $ 30-72
Dinner 晚膳
set 套餐 $ 108-168
à la carte 点菜 $ 120-250

■ **OPENING HOURS 营业时间**
Lunch 午膳 12:00-14:15 (L.O.)
Dinner 晚膳 18:00-22:00 (L.O.)

■ **ANNUAL AND WEEKLY CLOSING**
休息日期
Closed Tuesday 周二休息

SOUTH WEST 西南

♿ 🅿 ⇄18 ⏱

TEL. 6884 7888

**Hotel Michael, #02-142/143,
Resorts World Sentosa,
26 Sentosa Gateway**

圣淘沙桥门26号圣淘沙名胜世界
迈克尔酒店#02-142/143

www.tunglokheen.com

■ **PRICE 价钱**
Lunch 午膳
set 套餐 $ 48-100
à la carte 点菜 $ 40-85
Dinner 晚膳
set 套餐 $ 48-100
à la carte 点菜 $ 40-85

■ **OPENING HOURS 营业时间**
Lunch 午膳 11:30-14:00 (L.O.)
Dinner 晚膳 18:30-22:00 (L.O.)

🍴

TUNGLOK HEEN
同樂軒

Chinese • Contemporary
中国菜 • 时尚

Judicious lighting, dark wood and tones of red combine to give this contemporary Chinese restaurant at Sentosa's Hotel Michael a slick and stylish feel. In among the traditional Chinese dishes are others boasting surprisingly creative combinations, and presentation is always quite striking. Don't miss the double-boiled superior fish bone soup with fish maw; the roast duck; or the coconut jelly with crispy black forbidden rice.

设计时尚的餐室,予人轻松的感觉。供应的菜式不限于传统中菜,独特的创作与烹调风格和精致的卖相,带给食客新鲜感。不可不尝的除了鱼骨浓汤炖花胶外,还有伦敦烤鸭。甜品系列的椰皇脆紫米椰雪花同样出色。要在圣淘沙内找一家有素质的中菜馆,这儿绝对是其中一家值得考虑的。

HAWKER CENTRES
熟食小贩中心

Pasir Panjang Food Centre
巴西班让熟食中心

121 Pasir Panjang Road 巴西班让路121号

You may not see many visitors but this centre is popular with locals so this is a good choice. Conveniently close to the railway station, the centre hosts lots of seafood stalls. However, it is the mutton soup that makes it worth visiting.

闻名于本地人的熟食中心，反而较少游客到访，也许这样更能体会到地道的风味与口味，地点邻近地铁站，交通方便。中心内除了有大量烹调海鲜的食店，也有值得一试的羊肉汤。

IVY'S HAINANESE HERBAL MUTTON SOUP
海南藥材羊肉湯

Herbal mutton soup, herbal tendon soup and herbal tulang soup are delicious.
带有香浓药材味道的羊肉、羊筋與羊骨湯均十分美味。

STALL 铺 | #14 **PRICE** 价钱 | $ 10-25
OPENING HOURS 营业时间 | 11:30-21:00
Closed Sunday 周日休息

SOUTH WEST 西南

KhemChen/iStock

STREET FOOD
街头小吃

ZAI SHUN CURRY FISH HEAD
載順咖喱鱼头

A busy shop offering delicious fish and stir-fried dishes; curry fish head is their signature dish.

除了驰名咖喱鱼头外，各种鱼类菜式和小炒同样出色。

#01-205, 253 Jurong East Steet 24
裕廊东24街253号#01-205

PRICE 价钱 |
$ 10-30
OPENING HOURS 营业时间 |
07:00-15:00
Closed Wednesday 周三休息

HOTELS
酒店

SOUTH WEST 西南

Luxury · Contemporary
豪华·时尚

CAPELLA
嘉佩乐

A hotel fashioned from a restored colonial building, once used as an officers' mess, enveloped by a more contemporary structure designed by Foster + Partners; you'll find a charming library lounge in the former, and bedrooms in the latter. For those after a more tropical feel, there are also 38 villas with private plunge pools spread around the extensive grounds.

欲远离烦器？位于圣淘沙岛宁静角落的嘉佩乐是不二之选。它由两座风格迥异的建筑组成，曾是海防基地的殖民地建筑内设休息室和图书室；弧形现代建筑则是客房所在，由名师Norman Foster设计，房间宽敞，装潢雅致。有意尽情贴近大自然的，可选择被热带林围绕、备有户外淋浴和私人泳池的度假小屋。

TEL. 6377 8888
www.capellasingapore.com
1 The Knolls, Sentosa Island
圣淘沙岛诺尔思通道1号

61 **Rooms**/客房
51 **Suites**/套房
Price for 2 persons/双人房价格:
$ 620-1,200

TEL. 6808 7288
www.wsingaporesentosacove.com

21 Ocean Way
海洋大道21号

213 **Rooms**/客房
27 **Suites**/套房

Price for 2 persons/双人房价格:
$ 390-1,200

Resort • Design
渡假村 • 型格

W SENTOSA COVE

Those familiar with the brand will recognise many of the elements of this W hotel, which is located on the East side of Sentosa Island. There's the moodily-lit bedrooms with names like Wonderful, Spectacular and Fabulous; there's the lounge music that gives the hotel and its lobby such energy; and a young client base who are more interested in partying than peacefulness.

喜欢潮流艺术和好凑热闹的人，大概会爱上这间给棕榈树环抱、能欣赏港湾景色的酒店。奢华偌大的户外泳池、音韵缭绕充满情调的大堂，让你顷刻受到其气氛感染。住客可利用手机的应用软体办理入住手续，甚至打开房门。房间布置新颖细致，面向小港湾的客房景色较佳。能随意调校颜色的灯饰，让房间情调顿添。

Resort • Personalised
渡假村 • 个人化

EQUARIUS
逸濠

The most exciting bedrooms at this hotel – which is close to all the main attractions of Sentosa Island – are the 11 ocean suites: they offer spectacular views of Marine Life Park and make you feel you're living under the sea. The deluxe rooms are more soberly decorated but are spacious and well-equipped. If you want a tropical forest experience, book a 'beach villa'.

海景套房壮丽的海洋生物园景色，令人心感震撼，感觉犹如身处水底世界。豪华客房以米色及浅棕色为主调，风格素净，简约舒适。置身热带雨林是什么感觉？便要试试围绕泳池而建的海滨别墅。ESPA水疗中心提供多种能令你忘却烦忧的水疗和浸浴服务，饿了还能到中心内的水疗膳食餐厅尝尝美味健康的菜式。

TEL. 6577 6750
www.rwsentosa.com
Resorts World Sentosa,
8 Sentosa Gateway
圣淘沙桥门8号圣淘沙名胜世界

173 **Rooms**/客房
10 **Suites**/套房

Price for 2 persons/双人房价格:
$ 450-3,000

Recommended restaurants/餐厅推荐:
Forest 森 ⚫

SOUTH WEST 西南

♿ 🏊 **P** 🛎 🐕 ⛷ 🆂🅿🅰 💆

TEL. 6708 8310
www.sofitel-singapore-sentosa.com

2 Bukit Manis Road
武吉马尼斯路2号

174 **Rooms**/客房
41 **Suites**/套房

Price for 2 persons/双人房价格:
$ 315-890

🏠

Spa and wellness • Personalised
水疗 • 个人化

SOFITEL SENTOSA RESORT & SPA
圣淘沙索菲特

It's all about relaxation at this resort hotel perched on the cliff top above Tanjong Beach. It's surrounded by a tropical garden and has a delightful outdoor pool. The So SPA offers an impressive range of treatments as well as a restaurant with a health-conscious menu. Bedrooms are not particularly big but, thanks to some French design flair, they are very charming.

酒店于2015年翻新,法籍设计师用花朵和叶片在墙身和地毯作装饰,加上柔和灯光及暖色调布置的客房,面积虽称不上很大,却很温暖舒适。浴室用的是法国名牌用品。坐落于丹戎海滩之上,是其一大优点。面积偌大的So SPA内有逾二十个治疗室和户外水疗阁,还有瀑布泳池可供使用。酒店有专车往返水疗中心。

L. Serebrennikov / age fotostock

SOUTH EAST
东南

SOUTH EAST 东南

RESTAURANTS
餐厅

SIK BAO SIN (DESMOND'S CREATION)

吃飽先 Ⓝ

Singaporean • Simple
新加坡菜 • 简朴

The second-generation owner-chef of this restaurant makes every dish according to traditional recipes for an authentic taste. The menu features only 13 items, but he also cooks other seasonal dishes not on the menu. His recommendation, sweet and sour pork, takes 90 minutes to make. As he cooks every dish himself, expect to wait for up to 60mins for your food. Reservations are only accepted for groups of 10 people or more. The authentic home-style Cze Char is worth to wait.

出自服务客人的责任感,让东主坚持只用每天新鲜运抵的食材,烹调方式跟随传统食谱,以呈现原味。餐牌重质不重量,但若有时令食材,店主乐于另制菜式让客人尝鲜,皇牌菜式为酸甜肉,可是制作需时,不排除要等上九十分钟。餐厅只接受十位以上订座,而厨房工作由店主一手包办,故食客须耐心等候。

TEL. 6744 3757

592 Geylang Road
芽笼路592号

■ **PRICE 价钱**
Lunch 午膳
à la carte 点菜 $ 20-25
Dinner 晚膳
à la carte 点菜 $ 20-25

■ **OPENING HOURS 营业时间**
Lunch 午膳 11:45-13:45 (L.O.)
Dinner 晚膳 17:45-20:45 (L.O.)

■ **ANNUAL AND WEEKLY CLOSING**
休息日期
Closed 5 days before Lunar New Year, 6 days Lunar New Year; and Monday
农历年廿六至初六及周一休息

SOUTH EAST 东南

TEL. 6440 6786

135-137 East Coast Road
东海岸路135-137号

www.zaffronkitchen.com

■ **PRICE 价钱**
Lunch 午膳
set 套餐 $ 15-17
à la carte 点菜 $ 25-40
Dinner 晚膳
à la carte 点菜 $ 25-40

■ **OPENING HOURS 营业时间**
Lunch 午膳 11:30-14:30 (L.O.)
Dinner 晚膳 17:00-21:30 (L.O.)
Friday & Saturday dinner
周五及周六晚膳 17:00-22:30 (L.O.)
Sunday dinner 周日晚膳
17:00-22:00 (L.O.)

ZAFFRON KITCHEN (EAST COAST)

Indian • Contemporary
印度菜 • 时尚

Housed in a modern building on a busy road, this bright, modern Indian bistro comes with metal framed chairs, exposed brick walls, old tiles and an open kitchen. While the look and the technology used are very 21st century – menus are presented on an iPad – the cooking is much more traditional, with dishes from the tandoor being particularly tasty. The restaurant is also family-friendly and comes with a small play area for children.

橘红色的旧式砖墙、状似没修葺的天花、曝露在空气中的水管，予人返璞归真的味道。与其装潢一样，此店提供的传统北印度菜风味正宗。咖喱角(samosa)、天都里烤虾(tandoori jhinga)、香烤鸡块(chicken tikka)等均是北印度的传统菜式，也是此店名菜之一。店子内设有儿童小型玩乐场地，适合有小朋友的家庭。

CHILLI PADI (JOO CHIAT)
辣椒香（如切）

Peranakan • Oriental décor
娘惹菜 • 东方

For anyone wishing to explore the Peranakan culture, coming to Joo Chiat is a must – while you're there, you'll find this restaurant is the ideal place in which to taste authentic Peranakan dishes. The friendly staff are on hand to offer helpful advice, with the standout dishes being kueh pai ti, ikan assam and ayam rendang. The red-hued walls, Chinese furnishings and ceiling fans add to the atmosphere.

如切区是探索娘惹文化的必到之地，而位于区内的这家店子便是品尝娘惹菜的理想之处。红墙壁与大红印花桌布、中式摆设和木吊扇，充满浓浓的南洋气息。图文并茂的餐单，方便食客点选菜式，友善的店员也乐于为食客效劳。惹味开胃的娘惹花篮饼、酸辣阿参鱼和香浓的鸡仁当均是不能错过的经典菜肴。

TEL. 6275 1002
#01-03, 11 Joo Chiat Place
如切坊11號#01-03

■ **PRICE** 价钱
Lunch 午膳
à la carte 点菜 $ 15-30
Dinner 晚膳
à la carte 点菜 $ 15-30

■ **OPENING HOURS** 营业时间
Lunch 午膳 11:00-14:30 (L.O.)
Dinner 晚膳 17:30-21:30 (L.O.)

SOUTH EAST 东南

🈂️ 🍴

TEL. 6744 4574

639 Lorong 33 Geylang
芽笼33巷639号

■ **PRICE** 价钱
Lunch 午膳
à la carte 点菜 $ 20-40
Dinner 晚膳
à la carte 点菜 $ 20-40

■ **OPENING HOURS** 营业时间
Lunch 午膳 11:30-14:30 (L.O.)
Dinner 晚膳 17:00-23:00 (L.O.)

■ **ANNUAL AND WEEKLY CLOSING**
休息日期
Closed Monday 周一休息

GEYLANG CLAYPOT RICE
芽籠瓦煲飯

Cantonese · Simple
粤菜 · 简朴

The house speciality and the location are both there in the name. This modestly decorated place with its round tables and plastic chairs is all about rice cooked in a claypot over charcoal – accompanied by sausage, salted fish, chicken or cured meat. Other Cantonese dishes are also on offer, such as their delicious bean curd 'prawn ball'. As the rice takes 30mins to cook, call ahead to book a table and pre-order your rice to shorten the waiting time.

餐厅位于芽笼保留区，两旁全是两层高的殖民地时期建筑，临街一面保留着昔日面貌。招牌菜是以炭火炮制、即叫即煮的粤式瓦锅煲仔饭，腊肠、膶肠、咸鱼、鸡、腊肉等材料集于一锅。此外还供应广式小菜、蒸海鲜等。因煲仔饭制作需时约三十分钟，建议先预订，让店方因应人数和到达时间准备煲仔饭。

🍴⃝

ROLAND
東皇

Singaporean • Simple
新加坡菜 • 简朴

In 1956 Mdm Cher Yam Tian created her famous chilli crab and, together with her husband Lim Choon Ngee, opened a small restaurant along the Kallang River. It now occupies a vast space atop a multi-storey carpark in Katong (with a hard-to-find entrance) and is run by the second and third generations. Chilli crab rightly remains the bestseller; other dishes to look out for are black sauce prawn, crispy baby squid and pomfret done in two ways.

要数新加坡美食，一定少不了辣椒螃蟹。这道由1956年面世以来一直为人乐道的菜式，是原创者，此店东主的祖母徐炎珍女士为了满足对食物要求特高的丈夫而创作的，谁想到后来竟成了家喻户晓的美食！除了这道有名的辣椒螃蟹，其他必吃的特色菜还包括黑酱油虾及双宝花枝油条。

🅿 ⇔200
TEL. 6440 8205
Block 89, #06-750, Marine Parade
马林百列中心89座#06-750
www.rolandrestaurant.com.sg

■ **PRICE** 价钱
Lunch 午膳
à la carte 点菜 $ 40-80
Dinner 晚膳
à la carte 点菜 $ 40-80

■ **OPENING HOURS** 营业时间
Lunch 午膳 11:30-14:00 (L.O.)
Dinner 晚膳 18:00-22:00 (L.O.)

SOUTH EAST 东南

HAWKER CENTRES
熟食小贩中心

Bedok Interchange Hawker Centre

208 New Upper Changi Road
新樟宜路上段208号

It moved to its current location in 2014 and the dining experience has been enhanced, thanks to amenities like wi-fi and a cashless payment system. Some popular tenants from the old address moved in too.

于2014年迁往现址后予人焕然一新之感,空间更为明亮宽敞,亦增设座位及诸如无线上网、无现金支付系统等。内有七十个摊档位置,不少是从旧址迁来的受欢迎店铺。

BEDOK CHWEE KUEH
勿洛水粿

The Chwee Kueh's stuffing contains chilli, preserved radish, dried shrimps and spring onion.

水粿加上由菜脯、葱、虾米、辣椒煮成的酱一起进食,更可以辣菜脯佐吃。

STALL 铺 | #01-19　**PRICE** 价钱 | $ 1-2
OPENING HOURS 营业时间 | 06:30-21:30

HOCK HAI (HONG LIM) CURRY CHICKEN NOODLE
福海（芳林）咖哩鸡面

Curry and satay flavours are available; ingredients are rich in flavour, with a slightly spicy soup.

可选择咖喱或沙爹口味,并备有三种面条,汤底微辣,材料味道浓重。

STALL 铺 | #01-58　**PRICE** 价钱 | $ 4-6
OPENING HOURS 营业时间 | 09:00-23:00

SOUTH EAST 东南

NEW WORLD MUTTON SOUP
新世界羊肉湯

Specialising in mutton soup, mutton Kway Teow and mutton meatballs.

专注制作羊肉菜式如羊排汤、羊肉粿条和羊肉丸等。

STALL 铺 | #01-23 **PRICE** 价钱 | $ 6-12
OPENING HOURS 营业时间 | 09:30-22:30
Closed Tuesday 周二休息

SOUTH EAST 东南

85 Fengshan Centre
凤山中心

85 Bedok North Street 4　勿洛北4街85号

A popular hawker market with locals, the somewhat inconvenient location stops no one from enjoying its renowned snacks like Bak Chor Mee, even at midnight. It's a 15-20 minute walk from the nearest railway station so consider a bus or taxi.

吸引本地人就算凌晨时份也无惧疲意要到场一饱口腹的，就是这享负盛名的熟食市场。不像市中心般便捷，由邻近的铁路站起步行约十五至二十分钟，不过如想一尝肉脞面的话，绝对值得来此处寻珍。

85 BEDOK NORTH FRIED OYSTER
勿洛北85蚝煎

Fried oysters, fresh cockle Kway Teow and fried Hokkien noodles are recommended.
蚝煎、鲜蛤粿条、福建虾面等，满足好尝海上鲜的食客。

STALL 铺 | #01-09/10　**PRICE 价钱** | $ 3-8
OPENING HOURS 营业时间 | 15:00-01:30

SHI WEI DA
食為大潮州糜

Its tofu, pork, pork liver and generous amounts of sauce are a real steal.
售卖沙爹米粉，价钱便宜，配料充足多样，沙爹酱货真价实且浓而不腻。

STALL 铺 | #01-41　**PRICE 价钱** | $ 3-4
OPENING HOURS 营业时间 | 17:00-00:00

SOUTH EAST 东南

XING JI ROU CUO MIAN
興記肉脞麵

The meatballs are strong in flavour, while the soup is mixed with fried lard and minced meat.

肉丸分量不少，且味道浓郁，汤底佐以炸猪油和肉碎。

STALL 铺 | #01-07　**PRICE** 价钱 | $ 3-4
OPENING HOURS 营业时间 | 14:30-01:00
Closed Thursday　周四休息

51 Old Airport Road Food Centre

旧机场路饮食中心

51 Old Airport Road 旧机场路51号

Established in the '70s, 51 Old Airport Road Food Centre is one of the most historic hawker centres in Singapore. There are more than 160 stalls, some of which are time-honoured names. Don't be surprised by the long queues.

于七十年代落成，拥有逾一百六十个熟食摊位，旧机场路饮食中心乃新加坡最具历史的熟食中心之一。故其受欢迎程度也不令人意外：旅客慕名而来，老饕知味重临，不少老字号的摊前均排了长长的人龙，想一尝美味需要预早前来。

BLANCO COURT FOOD CENTRE (3RD STOREY)

多丽哥粿汁

Trotter, pork intestine, pork tripe and Kway Chap are recommended.

推荐卤水猪脚、大肠、猪肚以及豆干、粿汁。

STALL 铺 | #01-135 **PRICE** 价钱 | $ 5-10
OPENING HOURS 营业时间 | 11:00-15:30
Closed Monday & Tuesday 周一及周二休息

HUA KEE HOUGANG FAMOUS WAN TON MEE

華記后港祖傳馳名雲吞麵

Dumplings, wontons and chicken feet noodles are all worth trying.

店内的水饺面、炸云吞面、凤爪面均值得一试。

STALL 铺 | #01-02 **PRICE** 价钱 | $ 4-6
OPENING HOURS 营业时间 | 08:00-22:00

SOUTH EAST 东南

LAO FU ZI FRIED KWAY TEOW
老夫子炒粿條

Cooked-to-order black or white fried Kway Teow with varied ingredients and nicely balanced flavours.

黑或白粿条即叫即炒，火候及配料十足，包括芽菜、鸡蛋、腊肠、蛳蚶等。

STALL 铺 | #01-12 **PRICE** 价钱 | $ 4-8
OPENING HOURS 营业时间 | 11:00-22:00

WHITLEY RD BIG PRAWN NOODLE
威利大虾面

Varied side ingredients include prawns, pork liver or pork ribs. Cooked-to-order, the soup is rich in prawn flavour.

面条提供虾肉、猪肝跟肉骨等多种配搭。即叫即煮，虾汤味浓。

STALL 铺 | #01-98 **PRICE** 价钱 | $ 4-15
OPENING HOURS 营业时间 | 07:00-22:00

XIN MEI XIANG ZHENG ZONG LOR MEE
新美香 (正宗) 卤麵

Serves flat noodles cooked al dente with a strongly seasoned soup.

扁面条烹调得质感适中，有嚼劲。汤底浓厚。

STALL 铺 | #01-116 **PRICE** 价钱 | $ 4-6
OPENING HOURS 营业时间 | 06:00-13:00
Closed Thursday 周四休息

Pasar 16@Bedok (Bedok South Food Centre)  柏夏坊

16 Bedok South Road 勿洛南路16号

Its spacious interior allows guests to escape from the crowds. There's a variety of food to choose from, but don't miss the most popular - fried Kway Teow.

在这富阳光气息名字下的是空间开扬的熟食中心,桌椅在中间整齐地铺展开来,没有拥挤感。五花八门的食档则在两侧。中心内食物的选择不少,但最为闻名就是炒粿条。

HILL STREET FRIED KWAY TEOW
禧街炒粿條

The fried Kway Teow has an intense flavour. Expect queues.

炒粿条味道浓郁,捧场者众。

STALL 铺 | #01-41 **PRICE** 价钱 | $ 4
OPENING HOURS 营业时间 | 11:00-17:00
Closed Monday 周一休息

HOCK SENG CHOON FISH BALL KWAY TEOW MEE
福成春鱼丸粿条面

Fish balls are tender and rich. The al dente noodles marry well with the fresh broth.

鱼蛋味浓软熟,面条有弹性,清汤鲜味突出。

STALL 铺 | #01-50 **PRICE** 价钱 | $ 3-5
OPENING HOURS 营业时间 | 11:00-21:00
Closed Thursday every two weeks
隔周于周四休息

SOUTH EAST 东南

STREET
FOOD
街头小吃

SIN HUAT EATING HOUSE
新發

Rice noodles with crab and fishcakes
are the signature dishes.

螃蟹米粉和鱼饼是招牌菜，原只肉蟹，与葱、
蒜、辣椒及米粉同煮，味道鲜美。

659/661 Lorong 35 Geylang
芽笼35巷659/661号

PRICE 价钱 |
$ 20-40
OPENING HOURS 营业时间 |
19:00-24:00

BIRDS OF PARADISE

Offers house-made gelato served with
a thyme cone; white chrysanthemum
and lychee raspberry flavour is
recommended.

以自制百里香甜筒盛着口味繁多的意式冰淇
淋，推介白菊花及荔枝覆盆子口味。

#01-05, 63 East Coast Road
东海岸路63号#01-05

PRICE 价钱 |
$ 5-10
OPENING HOURS 营业时间 |
12:00-22:00,
Friday & Saturday 周五及周六 12:00-22:30

Closed Monday 周一休息

eye_/iStock

TRADITIONAL HAIG ROAD PUTU PIRING

Offers putu piring which is house-made with rice flour and brown sugar and served with freshly shredded coconut.

由一班女工即场制作；以米粉和黄糖做成的白色小软糕，配以鲜椰丝进食。

Inside Mr Teh Tarik, 26 Changi Road
樟宜路26号Mr Teh Tarik内

PRICE 价钱 |
$ 2-4
OPENING HOURS 营业时间 |
08:00-20:00

CSP_schoolgirl/Fotosearch LBRF / age fotostock

NORTH EAST & NORTH WEST

东北及西北

RESTAURANTS
餐厅

VIOLET OON
Peranakan • Design
娘惹菜 • 型格

To enjoy genuinely local fare gather up friends or family and head down to this sister restaurant of Violet Oon's National Kitchen. Designed for sharing, the traditional Peranakan dishes use secret sauce recipes and blends of herbs for an extra touch of personality. If you want to learn more about the cuisine, the small open kitchen is sometimes used by Violet herself for hosting cookery classes.

充满特色的设计，悬挂在墙上的老旧手写食谱，令餐室更添优雅。小小的开放式厨房，是甜点师傅献艺的舞台，偶尔会是东主Violet Oon讲课的场地。餐厅供应的是百分百娘惹菜，特别之处是店内所有香料和酱汁均按照独有的秘方调制，亦是其食物味道与别家菜馆不同的原因。食物分量的设计宜于与伙伴共享。

🚗 🅿 ⇔12 🔧
TEL. 9834 9935
881 Bukit Timah Road
武吉知马路881号
www.violetoon.com

■ **PRICE** 价钱
Lunch 午膳
set 套餐 $ 40-60
à la carte 点菜 $ 35-70
Dinner 晚膳
set 套餐 $ 60-80
à la carte 点菜 $ 35-70

■ **OPENING HOURS** 营业时间
Lunch 午膳 12:00-14:30 (L.O.)
Dinner 晚膳 18:00-21:30 (L.O.)

■ **ANNUAL AND WEEKLY CLOSING**
休息日期
Closed Monday 周一休息

NORTH EAST & NORTH WEST 东北及西北

HAWKER CENTRES
熟食小贩中心

Chomp Chomp Food Centre
忠忠熟食中心

20 Kensington Park Road 肯新顿园路20号

It may not be as big as other hawker centres, but its fame is such that it was once voted the best hawker centre in Singapore. Queues and crowds are everywhere, but the food is worth waiting for and there are many local snacks you won't want to miss.

虽然规模未如其他著名熟食中心般大，但切勿小觑其魅力，门庭若市已成常态。中心曾于2017年经过修缮，地道食品种类应有尽有。附近有很多酒吧，而中心内大部份店子只在晚上营业，令这区成了晚上人群聚集地。

AH HOCK FRIED HOKKIEN NOODLES
亚福炒福建虾麵

Serves fried Hokkien noodles with shrimp and squid.

面条以虾及鱿鱼为配料。

STALL 铺 | #01-27 **PRICE** 价钱 | $ 3-5
OPENING HOURS 营业时间 | 18:00-00:00
Closing not fixed 不固定休

CHOMP CHOMP SATAY
忠忠沙爹

Opt for pork, chicken, mutton or ketupat served with pineapple sauce.

佐以凤梨酱的串烧，可选猪、鸡、羊或粽子。

STALL 铺 | #01-34 **PRICE** 价钱 | $ 6-10
OPENING HOURS 营业时间 | 16:00-00:30

NORTH EAST & NORTH WEST 东北及西北

filipe_lopes/iStock

20 Ghim Moh Road Market & Food Centre

锦茂巴刹熟食中心

Blk 20, Ghim Moh Road 锦茂路大牌20

Opened in 1978, this hawker centre is hugely popular in this neighbourhood due in part to the lack of other centres nearby. Some of its renowned stalls have been serving the community for years. Foodies will be amazed by the choice, ranging from Chwee Kueh to duck rice and porridge.

因周边缺少大规模的商贩中心，令到这所邻近荷兰村，开业于1978年的巴刹熟食中心在该区中更受欢迎。中心内有不少经营了数十年的老店，慕名而来的人流众多；内里美食由水粿到鸭饭粿条等均有售，选择众多。

CHUAN KEE BONELESS BRAISED DUCK
全記 N

Duck rice, noodles, Kway Teow and porridge are recommended.

配以卤鸭的饭、粥、粿条或面，值得一试。

STALL 铺 | #01-04 **PRICE** 价钱 | $ 3-5
OPENING HOURS 营业时间 | 10:00-20:00
Closed Thursday & last Sunday of each month
周四及每月最后一个周日休息

GHIM MOH CHWEE KUEH N
锦茂李老三傳統水粿

A Chwee Kueh shop with loyal customers and a long history.

老字号水粿，很受欢迎。

STALL 铺 | #01-54 **PRICE** 价钱 | $ 2-3
OPENING HOURS 营业时间 | 06:15-18:30

STREET FOOD
街头小吃

𝕐◯

SPRINGLEAF PRATA PLACE

Serves prata that comes with sweet or
savory filling. A good choice for
breakfast, lunch or as a dessert.

配料繁多的印度薄饼，有甜有咸，作为早、午
餐或甜品均是不错的选择。

1 Thong Soon Avenue
通顺道1号

PRICE 价钱 |
$ 2-13
OPENING HOURS 营业时间 |
07:00-00:00

NORTH EAST & NORTH WEST 东北及西北

MICHELIN IS CONTINUALLY INNOVATING FOR SAFER, CLEANER, MORE ECONOMICAL, MORE CONNECTED... BETTER ALL-ROUND MOBILITY.

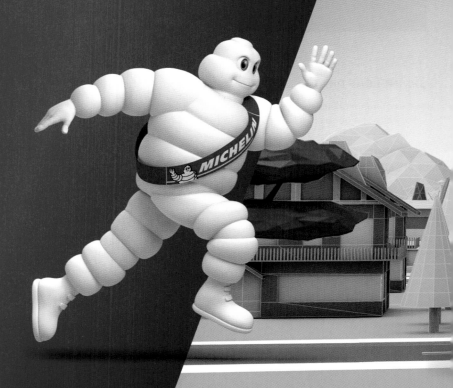

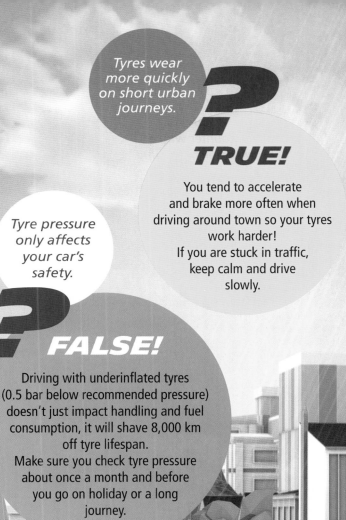

Tyres wear more quickly on short urban journeys.

TRUE!

You tend to accelerate and brake more often when driving around town so your tyres work harder!
If you are stuck in traffic, keep calm and drive slowly.

Tyre pressure only affects your car's safety.

FALSE!

Driving with underinflated tyres (0.5 bar below recommended pressure) doesn't just impact handling and fuel consumption, it will shave 8,000 km off tyre lifespan.
Make sure you check tyre pressure about once a month and before you go on holiday or a long journey.

Fitting **2 winter tyres** on my car guarantees maximum safety.

FALSE!

In the winter, especially when temperatures drop below 7°C, to ensure better road holding, all four tyres should be identical and fitted at the same time.

2 WINTER TYRES ONLY = risk of compromised road holding.

4 WINTER TYRES = **safer handling** when cornering, driving downhill and braking.

If you regularly encounter rain, snow or black ice, choose a **MICHELIN Alpin tyre**. This range offers you sharp handling plus a comfortable ride to safely face the challenge of winter driving.

MICHELIN
IS COMMITTED

▶ MICHELIN IS **GLOBAL LEADER IN FUEL-EFFICIENT TYRES** FOR LIGHT VEHICLES.

▶ **EDUCATING OF YOUNGSTERS IN ROAD SAFETY,** NOT FORGETTING TWO-WHEELERS. LOCAL ROAD SAFETY CAMPAIGNS WERE RUN IN **16 COUNTRIES** IN 2015.

QUIZ

1. TYRES ARE BLACK SO WHY IS THE MICHELIN MAN WHITE?

Back in 1898 when the Michelin Man was first created from a stack of tyres, they were made of natural rubber, cotton and sulphur and were therefore light-coloured. The composition of tyres did not change until after the First World War when carbon black was introduced. But the Michelin Man kept his colour!

2. FOR HOW LONG HAS MICHELIN BEEN GUIDING TRAVELLERS?

Since 1900. When the MICHELIN guide was published at the turn of the century, it was claimed that it would last for a hundred years. It's still around today and remains a reference with new editions and online restaurant listings in a number of countries.

3. WHEN WAS THE "BIB GOURMAND" INTRODUCED IN THE MICHELIN GUIDE?

The symbol was created in 1997 but as early as 1954 the MICHELIN guide was recommending "exceptional good food at moderate prices". Today, it features on the MICHELIN Restaurants website and app.

If you want to enjoy a fun day out and find out more about Michelin, why not visit the l'Aventure Michelin museum and shop in Clermont-Ferrand, France:
www.laventuremichelin.com

MICHELIN
A better way forward

索引
INDEX

STARRED RESTAURANTS

星级餐厅

❀ ❀

❀

BIB GOURMAND RESTAURANTS 😊
必比登美食推介餐厅

INDEX OF RESTAURANTS
餐厅列表

RESTAURANTS BY CUISINE TYPE
餐厅 — 以菜式分类

SINGAPOREAN/新加坡菜

PERANAKAN/娘惹菜

ASIAN CONTEMPORARY/时尚亚洲菜

AUSTRALIAN CONTEMPORARY/时尚澳洲菜

BARBECUE/烧烤

CALIFORNIAN/加州菜

CANTONESE/粤菜

CANTONESE ROAST MEATS/烧味

CHINESE/中国菜

EUROPEAN/欧陆菜

EUROPEAN CONTEMPORARY/时尚欧陆菜

FRENCH/法国菜

RESTAURANTS WITH PRIVATE ROOMS
有私人厢房的餐厅

INDEX OF HAWKER CENTRES
熟食小贩中心列表

306

TANJONG PAGAR PLAZA MARKET & FOOD CENTRE/ 丹戎巴葛坊小贩中心

TEKKA CENTRE/竹脚中心

TIONG BAHRU MARKET/中峇鲁市场

20 GHIM MOH ROAD MARKET & FOOD CENTRE/ 锦茂巴刹熟食中心

WHAMPOA MAKAN PLACE/黄埔熟食中心

ZION RIVERSIDE FOOD CENTRE/锡安河畔食阁

INDEX OF STREET FOOD
街头小吃列表

INDEX OF HOTELS
酒店列表

CREDITS:

MICHELIN TRAVEL PARTNER

Société par actions simplifiées au capital de 15 044 940 €
27 Cours de L'Île Seguin - 92100 Boulogne Billancourt (France)
R.C.S. Nanterre 433 677 721

E-mail : michelinguide.singapore@michelin.com

Welcome to RobertParker.com!

For more than 38 years,
Robert Parker Wine Advocate has established
itself as the independent fine wine guide on the
international scene and is seen today as
the most influential wine review globally.

Receive the WINE ADVOCATE bi-monthly digital review
and access over 10 years of archives with a fully
searchable database of 285,000 tasting notes, scores,
articles and reviews.

Enjoy the member's benefits brought to you by our
Global Membership Programme that will reward
you with special gourmet and wine experiences
offered by our retail and F&B partners, and provide
you a privileged access to our worldwide series of events
"Matter of Taste".

To activate your free one-year online membership
(valued at USD99) to The Wine Advocate and MICHELIN
guide Singapore, simply use the code below and register
on RobertParker.com and guide.michelin.sg.

MGSGmK5jg5